On The Plus Side

Thoughts on Mathematics and its Teaching

Chris Pritchard

THE SCOTTISH MATHEMATICAL COUNCIL

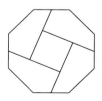

On the Plus Side: Thoughts on Mathematics and its Teaching

ISBN: 978-1-3999-8226-9

FOREWORD

Dr Chris Pritchard has been heavily involved with the Scottish Mathematical Council (SMC) for many years. He served as its Chair from 2014 to 2019. During this time he established the SMC as an important player in Scottish education, notably in connection with Maths Week Scotland. Chris edited the *SMC Journal* for 18 years and also established the *Primary Journal*. During that period he revolutionised the appearance of the *SMC Journal* with an attractive cover and a two-column format, as well as soliciting articles of interest to a wide audience.

Chris loves writing and has published numerous books and articles. It is therefore highly appropriate that the SMC should publish a collection of Chris's writings. Most of the articles appeared originally in the *SMC Journal*.

In the first chapter we read about how Chris adapted to moving from a large comprehensive school in London to a school in South Uist. Standard Grade was being introduced and it was a challenge to make the contents of the Mathematics syllabus relevant to the students in this small island school. We also hear about the early days of the SMC and some of the people involved, notably a Glaswegian who became one of the world's great recreational mathematicians.

The second chapter discusses the importance of sound and vision in aiding learners' understanding. For example, delivery by the teacher should be "clear but replete with tonal colour". The discussion of language mentions palindromes, anagrams and other things familiar to crossword buffs. The latter part of the chapter is based on Chris's Presidential Address at the Annual Conference of The Mathematical Association in 2022. Things turn cerebral as we learn aspects of how the brain works. The importance of diagrams is emphasised. (That having been said, there was a geometry professor who gave his lectures in total darkness, so that students could not see any diagrams but had to visualise things in their minds!)

The next two chapters discuss closed and open-ended mathematical problems respectively. For a number of years the SMC has contributed daily problems during Maths Week Scotland. A selection of 25 of these problems, all composed by Chris, is presented (with solutions at the end of the chapter). Chris encourages us all to be creative and not to stick to problems in books. The first problem in the chapter is an admirable example, with a quirkiness which should make the reader smile.

The fourth chapter presents open-ended problems in five contexts which provide ample scope for investigations. The section involving tetrominoes of different shapes is accessible to primary pupils as well as secondary. We all know that in chess the queen is the most powerful piece but we may ask if it is possible to quantify this and decide whether the knight is more powerful than the bishop or vice versa. One possible numerical measure of power is proposed but the reader can try to come up with others.

"Geometry is not well represented in the curriculum these days". What many would regard as an understatement begins the fifth chapter, which is devoted to cyclic quadrilaterals. Pupils nowadays get very little exposure to the beautiful geometry of the humble triangle. After a very brief summary of what they are missing, Chris investigates whether there are analogues for a cyclic quadrilateral and gives an elegant presentation of a series of results which will be unfamiliar to most readers.

The final chapter takes us back in time. Rubbing shoulders with the famous names of Archimedes with his tangrams, Christopher Wren with the cycloid and William Playfair with his statistical diagrams, we find John Mair, a teacher who founded Perth Academy. He wrote a remarkable book, simply entitled Arithmetic. In it you will read all about casting out nines and extracting square roots, and even cube roots, by hand. The final part of the chapter is devoted to Peter Guthrie Tait and his work on the flight of a golf ball, at the end of which there is a photo of Chris holding a piece of apparatus which Tait used in his experiments.

The History of Mathematics is one of Chris's major interests. Although the final chapter is explicitly devoted to this topic, historical references abound throughout the book. The reader will soon realise that a huge amount of research has been undertaken in its preparation and that Chris has produced what can fairly be regarded as a book that is eminently readable and a work of great scholarship.

Adam McBride

DEDICATION

This book is dedicated to my grandchildren:

Martha, Ewan & Jonah Smith;

Caleb Alwande Pritchard;

Lachlan, Blair & Penelope Pritchard;

Flynn, Ralph, Grace & Skye Campbell.

ACKNOWLEDGEMENT

It has been a real pleasure to pull together this book and I hope that whether you are teaching in a primary school, a secondary mathematics department, or a college or university, you will find something in it that will either help shape your thinking about mathematics learning and teaching or you can make use of directly in the classroom. So I am most grateful to the Scottish Mathematical Council and its Chair, Dr Alan Walker, for giving me the opportunity and for funding the project. I also really appreciate the efforts of those who checked what I produced initially and offered their constructive comments on where improvements might be made. They are Simon Fogiel, Paul Argyle McDonald, Sue Pope, Tom Roper and Alan Walker. Finally, my thanks to Adam McBride not just for penning the Foreword but for being such an inspiration to mathematics teachers over the years.

CONTENTS

Chapter 5: Cyclic Quadrilaterals

Chapter 6: History of Mathematics

1 The Scottish Mathematical Council

1.1 Where it all began

My wife, Audrey, and I arrived on South Uist on the overnight ferry from Oban to Lochboisdale three days after Christmas Day in 1982. We had each taught for over six years in the Wanstead area of north-east London, she in special education and, in my case, in a very large multicultural comprehensive, so we were fully aware that living and teaching in this remote, rural community would be a whole new experience. The person who was meant to meet us on the quayside was 'unwell', which apparently can be the case over Christmas and the New Year, and a Council worker was called on to break into the house the Council had set aside for us, kindly returning later to repair the damage.

For those unfortunate souls who have never been to the Western Isles, they are stunning. South Uist is long and thin and runs north-south. When travelling the main, spinal road, the locals say they are going "down north" or "up south". The Atlantic coast on the west has long sweeping strands, while the east coast consists of rocky coves, and in between there is the fertile machair where the 'yellow flags' wave in the late spring and the elusive corncrakes, unlike Victorian children, are heard but not seen. We soon got used to howling winds (two days in three on average) and to the wealth of wildlife – porpoises at Pollachar, seals at Smercleit, otters at Eynort, a range of waders sufficient to delight the most curmudgeon of ornithologists, gannets darting into the ocean with impressive power and precision, and whooper swans sailing gracefully on the lochans. From the sublime to the ridiculous, we feasted on salmon, crabs and lobster but also survived the stalest of bread and unwisely experienced a local delicacy, cormorant. We ventured to Lewis and Harris one weekend but Stornoway was closed and we survived on the biscuits we had brought with us. But of course, there was *uisge beatha gu leór*, strictly 'a sufficiency of whisky', rather than a glut.

On our first full day on the island, an old man touched his forelock as he passed me by. He knew I was the new dominie and this was his way of showing respect – a left-over from another era, maybe, but a charming one nevertheless. Daliburgh School was a 5-16 establishment, a tenth the size of my London school, and I joined a management team of Tom Rankin, an excellent Head, his Depute and two other Principal Teachers (English and Science). My immediate colleague was Catriona Walker, a local, Gaelic-speaking, mathematics teacher. The mathematics curriculum culminated in O Grade Mathematics for the 'most able', O Grade Arithmetic for the middle band and nothing, or at least nothing in a formal sense, for the 'least able'. It was not a set-up for which I had any sympathy. It applied the notion of a standard (O Grade) inconsistently in that the Mathematics and Arithmetic examinations were set at totally different difficulty levels, and it institutionalised the idea that qualifications are inappropriate for some members of society. Evidence of this archaic model was also manifest in the continuing use of the Lochgelly tawse.

Thankfully, the tawse would soon be phased out and the curriculum would be completely revamped with the introduction of Standard Grades for all in a new, enlightened conception of Scottish education. Examinations would be set at three levels (Foundation, General and Credit), with pupils typically tackling two adjacent levels. There were many sceptical voices, plenty of teachers who didn't want to grasp the nettle, some because of philosophical misgivings, some through inertia or lethargy – they say that there's no word in Gaelic that describes anything so immediate as *mañana* – but I saw the prospect of something much better than the status quo. And so it was that I started writing materials for the new courses and that led to my being approached by Gerry McKaig, the editor of the *Scottish Mathematical Council Newsletter*, as the *Journal* was then called, to write my first article. Excerpts from that 1985 article are reprinted below and the three sections that then follow relate to the Scottish Mathematical Council more generally.

1.2 Standard Grade mathematics: the story so far
SMC Newsletter 15 (1985), pp. 46-53; edited extract

... From the outset, it seemed clear that the introduction of Standard Grade curricula would have the widest and most profound implications for those pupils who have been labelled 'less able'. Consequently, we felt that most of our industry should be directed towards the formulation of a suitable course for Foundation level.

Designing a syllabus for use in a rural school

The teaching of mathematics in urban Glasgow and in rural communities, such as here in South Uist, is by necessity, different. Take, for example, the topic of traffic. A perfectly valid exercise in Glasgow, such as the collecting of data about vehicles as they pass the school, would be nonsense here. In a half-hour stint, only a dozen recordings might be made and perhaps a particular vehicle would be included three times.

Even more pertinent is the background knowledge of the pupils who have never been to the city. Few pupils in South Uist could quote the sequence, "red, red and amber, green, amber, and back to red", which is so familiar to the urban youngster. Not one member of a class of eight Foundation pupils I taught recently had any conception of a flyover. On the other hand, some children in South Uist can convert from hectares to acres and vice versa and will demonstrate what is meant by a fathom by stretching an imaginary rope across their chests.

These days, it is widely accepted that the acquisition of mathematical skills is facilitated when they are set in real-life contexts. This raises the question,

"Which contexts should be used?" Our belief is that the more familiar the context, the better. This is particularly true of Foundation level. Consequently, the content of many of our units has been determined by the local environment. Perhaps the employment of a blatant oversimplification will be helpful in illustrating our approach to the design of the syllabus. South Uist is a

REMOTE, WINDSWEPT, GAELIC-SPEAKING, FARMING community.

These stark adjectives lead conveniently to the construction of a 'syllabus influence diagram' like the one shown on the next page. The content of each unit is outlined, along with the level for which it is intended. Some of the units were written by colleagues in neighbouring schools.

This building of a core of units which have local interest was carried out early in our preparation of the syllabus. We have since added flesh to this skeleton, abiding strictly by the rule that the context must be relevant to the pupil for whom it is intended. Many of these subject areas, like the world of sport in which numbers are ubiquitous, are of interest to pupils from all parts of the country. To discuss them at length here would be to depart from one of the main purposes of this essay which is to highlight the differences between urban and rural approaches to the implementation of Standard Grade mathematics. The extent to which we feel our method of syllabus construction has been a success, will be discussed later.

Those pupils whom we would have classified in the past as suitable candidates for the 'O' grade mathematics examination were relieved to discover that the differences between the Credit and 'O' grade syllabuses are not substantial. One or two topics have been dropped: a couple have been inserted to take their place. However, ... the 'O' grade syllabus is now seen as bringing to mathematics teaching an aridity of Saharan proportions. Yes, a body of knowledge is imparted and many pupils pass their examinations, but at what expense? Have we not produced, in these successful candidates, young people who can "do" mathematics rather than be mathematicians?

The time has come for new initiatives to be taken in the teaching of those pupils who have some feel for the subject. A problem-solving approach has been successful in America and material is now being introduced into Scottish schools. Unfortunately, many teachers here may be unfamiliar with techniques which foster an ability to solve problems by using non-algorithmic strategies. ... One of the units in which we have taken a problem-solving approach is 'Effie, the Mathematical Goat', described briefly in the syllabus influence diagram. For the duration of the first week, Effie is tethered to a stake. It is up to the pupils to determine the shape and hence the area of the plot of land that she may graze. By moving the stake, from week to week, so that the goat's freedom of movement is further curtailed by appropriately-positioned walls and fences, pupils are introduced to locus questions and to the arithmetic of the sector and the segment, as if by accident.

SYLLABUS INFLUENCE DIAGRAM

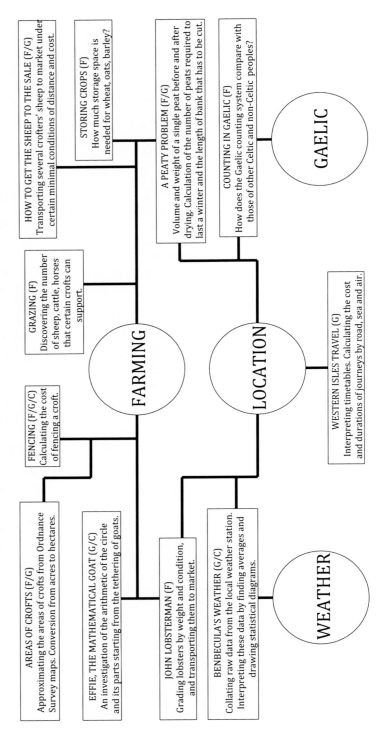

HOW TO GET THE SHEEP TO THE SALE (F/G)
Transporting several crofters' sheep to market under certain minimal conditions of distance and cost.

STORING CROPS (F)
How much storage space is needed for wheat, oats, barley?

A PEATY PROBLEM (F/G)
Volume and weight of a single peat before and after drying. Calculation of the number of peats required to last a winter and the length of bank that has to be cut.

COUNTING IN GAELIC (F)
How does the Gaelic counting system compare with those of other Celtic and non-Celtic peoples?

GAELIC

GRAZING (F)
Discovering the number of sheep, cattle, horses that certain crofts can support.

FARMING

LOCATION

WESTERN ISLES TRAVEL (G)
Interpreting timetables. Calculating the cost and durations of journeys by road, sea and air.

FENCING (F/G/C)
Calculating the cost of fencing a croft.

AREAS OF CROFTS (F/G)
Approximating the areas of crofts from Ordnance Survey maps. Conversion from acres to hectares.

EFFIE, THE MATHEMATICAL GOAT (G/C)
An investigation of the arithmetic of the circle and its parts starting from the tethering of goats.

JOHN LOBSTERMAN (F)
Grading lobsters by weight and condition, and transporting them to market.

BENBECULA'S WEATHER (G/C)
Collating raw data from the local weather station. Interpreting these data by finding averages and drawing statistical diagrams.

WEATHER

We have changed our position too with regard to rigour. There are some areas of the syllabus for which a less rigorous, more intuitive approach to mathematics teaching is suitable. ... At Daliburgh now, Credit and General level pupils learn the formulas for the circumference and area of a circle in S3 in the following ways: $C = \pi d$ is derived from $C/d = \pi$, a relationship which is discovered empirically by rolling tins of beans, steak and kidney pie and hot-dog sausages, and recording the distances travelled in one revolution. An accurate value for π is not essential at this stage, but we generally get quotients of 3.15 or 3.16. It is more important that the class be convinced that the ratio of circumference to diameter is constant.

The 'toilet roll' method of discovering the area of a circle is visually impressive. It did not originate with me, I am sorry to report. Nevertheless, I would like to pass it on because ... it is not well-known. If you can find a roll of paper which does not have a hole in the middle, all the better. If not, then the imagination is called into play.

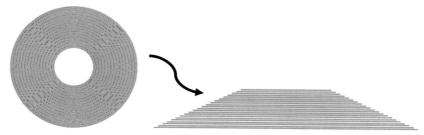

Cut down through the roll into the centre at right angles to the direction that it unrolls. (A carpet knife is a suitable cutting instrument.) Place your fingers inside the cut and open it out until it flops down on both sides. An ordinary toilet roll unfurls to give a shape whose cross-section is an isosceles trapezium, as pictured above. But if there is no central hole, the result is a triangular prism, whose end is an isosceles triangle of height r and base $2\pi r$.

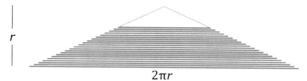

r

$2\pi r$

Since the area of the original circle is approximately equal to the area of the 'triangle',

$$\text{Area of circle} \approx \frac{1}{2} \times 2\pi r \times r = \pi r^2.$$

It is reassuring to discover that in the years prior to the birth of the calculus, the work of Pierre de Fermat and John Wallis contained such step integrations. They were necessary intuitive precursors of the rigorous calculus and even more rigorous analysis to come. If the young mathematician is to progress to the rigorous in mathematics he will need to pass through this intuitive stage.

The present and the future

During the course of this year at Daliburgh, Foundation level pupils have been shaken out of their lethargy and disinterest. Their extrinsic motivation has been bolstered by the dangling of a carrot in the guise of a nationally recognised certificate. Furthermore, the realisation on their part, that they too can do mathematics and thereby gain some pleasure from seeing that their environment and their mathematics are inextricably linked is evidence of increased intrinsic motivation. This, in itself, is a joy to behold. We have more work to do at Credit and General levels. Trigonometry has caused us particular problems because in South Uist there is a paucity of man-made structures of substantial height and only a handful of trees. There is no point in using trigonometry to measure something whose height or length is known. As a group of techniques, its merit lies in its ability to offer opportunities to measure the inaccessible. We will be out on the shore, in the next few months, using our plastic theodolites to find how far out at sea certain rocks lie—a sort of lateral, rather than vertical trigonometry.

...

Let me leave you with some words of wisdom which I read recently in *The Spell of Mathematics* by W. J. Reichman:

> It is given but to few men to know the triumphant ecstasy of original mathematical discovery. The distant peaks are hidden from all but these fortunate few. Those who conquer mighty mountains are the giants of mountaineering, but there are countless others throughout the world indulging their love of rock climbing. They climb rocks because they enjoy doing it, and the Everest man is still a rock climber at heart.

> There is plenty of mathematical climbing to do and the magical view of the peaks, once discerned, provides a powerful temptation to keep on climbing. There is an infinity in the variety of views which open up at different levels, and many side routes, invisible from lower levels, offer tantalizing invitations away from the main routes.

We believe that imaginatively devised courses, developed within the framework of Standard Grade mathematics, will offer such vistas. The mists which sometimes cover our beautiful hills are already lifting.

1.3 The inaugural Scottish Mathematical Council
SMC Journal 47 (2017), p. 35; extended

When the Scottish Mathematical Council was established in September 1967, its membership consisted of fifteen men and no women. There were five academic mathematicians, Robert Rankin (1915–2001) and John Hunter (1922–2013) of Glasgow University, Arthur Erdélyi (1908–1977) and James Fulton of Edinburgh University and Iain Adamson (1928–2010) of Dundee University. There were also two representatives from industry, Dr J King of the Naval Construction Research Establishment in Dunfermline and Tom O'Beirne, the subject of the next section of this chapter. The Inspectorate was represented by A G Robertson, and there was a member from a college of education and a technical college. There were five teachers, four from independent schools and just one from a state school. Rankin was the first Chairman. (Moves towards the gender-neutral 'Chair' were a long way off.)

The names of the mathematicians may not be well known to today's mathematics teachers but what is clear is that they were serious mathematicians of national if not international renown. They had a particular interest in the upper secondary years of school mathematics because that was the proving ground for their future university students. John Hunter, for example, wrote or co-wrote three books for those seeking matriculation: *Calculus*, *Analytic Geometry and Vectors* and *Algebra and Number Systems*, all in the Sixth Form Mathematics Series published by Blackie for the Scottish Mathematics Group. It appears that that first Scottish Mathematical Council had little focus on the education of primary children.

Of the pure mathematicians two stand out. Arthur Erdélyi was a Hungarian mathematician with expertise in Special Functions, especially the hypergeometric function, who came to Edinburgh to escape Nazi persecution. He subsequently spent short periods in the States before being offered a chair at Edinburgh alongside Alec Aitken, who was then in failing health.

Robert Rankin (shown alongside) was educated at Fettes College and Clare College, Cambridge. His early research led to collaboration with G. H. Hardy on the results of Ramanujan. This work was interrupted by the War during which Rankin worked on rocket trajectories. Later, he lectured at Cambridge, before being offered a chair at Birmingham, and subsequently a chair at Glasgow University where his research interests were dominated by the theory of numbers and the theory of functions. Throughout his career, Robert Rankin was keenly interested in the history of mathematics and so
perhaps there is no surprise that my only contact with him occurred when I spoke on the life and work of the Victorian mathematician Peter Guthrie Tait at the Glasgow Mathematical Association in the 1990s. I remember his kind words at the end of that talk to this day. (Incidentally, the final section of this book takes us back to Tait and his golf-ball aerodynamics.)

There were also two mathematicians with mechanics or engineering expertise, James King and Tom O'Beirne. In the 1950s, King had been the Chief Scientist at the Naval Construction Research Establishment at Rosyth where his team carried out experiments on the strength of materials used in submarines and aircraft carriers. Within months of the Scottish Mathematical Council being established he was appointed Regius Professor of Engineering at Edinburgh University, so had both an academic and an applied scientific background. And then there was Tom O'Beirne ...

1.4 Tom O'Beirne: Scotland's great recreational mathematician

This section is based on my article in SMC Journal 47 (2017), pp. 30-32. It has been extended and enhanced recently using additional information and impressions gratefully received from Tom's daughters, Ruth Sharp and her sister Judith.

O'Beirne's career

Fifty years ago, Thomas Hay O'Beirne (1915–1982), known as Tom O'Beirne, was a mathematician at Barr and Stroud Ltd., an optical engineering firm based in Anniesland, producing binoculars and rangefinders for the Royal Navy and much else besides. He also sported a substantial reputation as a recreational mathematician. As we have seen, in 1967, he was invited to be one of the founding members of the Scottish Mathematical Council.

O'Beirne was educated at Hillhead High School. His initial plan was to study Classics at University until in his second last year at school he contracted meningitis. His illness kept him away from school for a whole year but while he was recuperating he became interested in mathematics. When he returned to his last year at school, he put his energies into studying mathematics, ending the year not only with the prize for that subject but as Dux of the School. (Such was his brilliance that he'd taken the prizes for English, Latin and Greek as well!) On the back of these results, O'Beirne was awarded one of the major entrance bursaries to Glasgow University to study Mathematics and Natural Philosophy (i.e. Physics) and he graduated M.A. in 1938.

During the war years and beyond O'Beirne worked for the Royal Navy Scientific Service, and then briefly as a scientific officer with the Ordnance Survey. Through the 1950s and 1960s he led a team of mathematicians at Barr and Stroud, finally leaving the company in 1971 to lecture in the computing department at Glasgow University. By this time, Barr and Stroud had been working hand-in-hand with the university for over a decade as they attempted to diversify into electronics and, as we shall see, Tom O'Beirne was a key player in that collaboration.

Pioneering electronic music

From 1958 to 1963, Barr and Stroud and Glasgow University worked on a project to produce Scotland's first 'mini-computer' (the size of a desk). SOLIDAC (= **SOLID**-state **A**utomatic **C**omputer) was designed by Paul Thomas and built by O'Beirne. It afforded undergraduates first-hand experience of what was then the latest technology. O'Beirne was much taken with this machine and within a couple of years was using it to produce music with a stochastic twist.

O'Beirne, with Solidac in 1969

Bill Finlay, later a lecturer at Glasgow University, had an encounter with Tom O'Beirne at an impressionable age:

> 'In 1965 a public lecture was given by Tom (T.H.) O'Beirne, on the topic *Music, Numbers, and Computers* (the *Bull. Inst. Math. Appl.* later published a paper with the same title). Tom O'Beirne was a 'character' of the old school, such as one seldom encounters these days ... Since music, numbers, and computers were three of my great interests, I attended his lecture. At the end of the talk Tom invited the audience to a demonstration. I took part, and was allowed to flick handswitches and enter numbers on the SOLIDAC console, which had a telephone dial for the easy input of decimal data. This was quite a thrill for a nerdy 17-year-old, half a century ago!

> 'Thanks to Tom's virtuoso programming in machine code, SOLIDAC was capable of impressive feats in the automated composition and performance of music. This resulted in the release of an LP album that was reviewed in *Gramophone*. In later years Tom joined the Department of Computing Science at Glasgow University, where he lavished care on SOLIDAC, keeping it operational well beyond its natural lifespan.'

And while the computer itself was kept going for a long time, much of the music Tom O'Beirne programmed it to compose and play is still available to all on the internet. *A Small Computer Plays Some Samples of Mozart's Dice-composition Music* can be accessed via

https://physicalimpossibility.com/2013/01/05/1967-computer-music-produced-in-glasgow/

and some of Solidac's bagpipe music, entitled *Enneadic Selections* can be found at www.youtube.com/watch?v=qXbK5k4MZ1s. O'Beirne also programmed Haydn dice-music, Indian ragas and some very complicated peels of bells.

Now the sounds produced by Solidac might be described as tinny, rather than characteristic of the clarinet (as claimed), but that is not the point for, clearly, the combination of electronics, music and probability constituted ground-breaking research and development putting Glasgow, for a while, at the cutting edge of electronic music. It was something only a polymath such as Tom O'Beirne could have pulled off.

And it didn't go unnoticed! *Cybernetic Serendipity* was an exhibition of cybernetic art shown at the Institute of Contemporary Arts in London in the autumn of 1968, moving on the following year to Washington and San Francisco. O'Beirne was asked to give a demonstration and, as a result, his electronic bagpipe music appeared on the album, *Cybernetic Serendipity Music* alongside the likes of John Cage who also made use of randomness (though not computers) when composing some of his music.

Recreational mathematics

As a recreational mathematician, O'Beirne left a legacy few could match. He was probably hooked on mathematical problems and puzzles at a young age, certainly from university onwards. It seems that during his early professional life – when his daughters, Ruth and Judith, were growing up – these engaging intellectual challenges were something of an obsession. Ruth remembers that her father

> 'would spend every evening and well into the early morning sitting behind his table with papers spread out in front of him and perhaps also on the floor beside him, listening with half an ear to what we were all talking about or watching on television … Thinking back now, I realise that he tried out all his puzzle ideas on his family as the first audience … though when we were young he explained things in too much detail – or we did not have enough patience – and we had all sorts of other interests of our own to pursue. Nevertheless, we are both mentioned in *Puzzles and Paradoxes* [discussed below] and we could certainly do most of the wooden building block puzzles and anything that seemed like a jigsaw to us. I recall that I was particularly good at the Tantalizer!'

By the time he reached his early forties, O'Beirne had a gained something of a reputation in this area because, with a nod to Matrtin Gardner's mathematics column which had appeared in *Scientific American* since December 1956, he was invited by the editor of *New Scientist* to do something similar this side of the pond. O'Beirne's column, 'Puzzles and paradoxes' ran for sixty weeks (from 5 January 1961 to 22 February 1962) and, incidentally, these issues all are available online free of charge courtesy of *Google Books*. Tom's profile appeared at the back of the first issue to which he contributed. Among the details given were that 'he reads light verse, plays and detective fiction, and can sometimes be induced to work in his own garden when not inventing puzzles'. His first column starts on the very next page (p. 48) and includes these words: 'Quite a few recreations are 'mathematical' by courtesy only – the main need may only be for careful logical reasoning of the type which can form part of the attraction of a good detective novel'.

It is worth quoting some passages in full from O'Beirne's lengthy introduction justifying the need for a column on recreational mathematics in *New Scientist*.

> 'Not everyone, we know, finds mathematics an immediately attractive subject of interest. Some will admit that it may be important, and perhaps engrossing, to those who apply it in science, industry, commerce or finance. Many will assert that they themselves are 'hopeless' at mathematics.
>
> 'This seems doubly wrong, and more than a pity. The truth is that the true mathematician pursues beauty as much as – or more than – utility. It may be an austere form of beauty, like the clear, hard appeal of a diamond, but it is there. As with many forms of beauty, those who appreciate it have a strong urge to bring others to share their experience, in what measure they can.
>
> 'This may be easier than many think, and recreational material may be the thin end of the necessary wedge. We feel that many people are non-mathematical only for lack of suitable bait at the appropriate time – school, or later.'

The first problem he presents is well known and has been given in various versions over a surprisingly long period of time. O'Beirne explains that its title, *Laetitiae causa*, which translates as 'for your enjoyment', will form an 'excellent motto to begin our series'.

Puzzles and paradoxes

by T. H. O'Beirne

1 : *"Laetitiae causa"*

AT the start of a new weekly series, it seems only fair to give prospective readers some idea of what type of material they may expect to find regularly in it. The first article is a natural place to look for an indication of the author's philosophy, policy, idiosyncrasies or just plain prejudices. Here this has the further advantage of employing the space which in later articles will make reference back to the discussion or problem of the previous week.

To begin with our main title : a puzzle will mean any problem whose method of solution is not (we will hope) immediate or obvious; and a paradox will mean something whose truth and explanation can be established only in the face of some initial

He traces *Laetitiae causa* to an eighth century letter from Alcuin of Northumbria to his pupil, the Emperor Charlemagne, but gives the problem in the form used by Charles Hutton in 1803:

> 'Three jealous husbands with their wives having to cross a river at a ferry, find a boat without a boatman; but the boat is so small that it can contain no more than two of them at once. How can these six persons cross the river so than none of the women shall be left in company with any of the men, unless when her husband is present?'

The challenge is left for readers until the following week and O'Beirne comments that 'those who solve it should be able to prove that four or more couples cannot impose similar restrictions and still cross the river'.

Certainly, from the 1960s onwards and perhaps before, Tom O'Beirne was in correspondence with numerous mathematicians interested in or actively involved in the recreational side of the subject. He was a firm friend of Martin Gardner with whom he carried on a lively exchange. Letters would also come into the family home from the geometer Donald Coxeter, the chess puzzlist Richard Guy and the games designer Wade E Philpott, all based in Canada; also from Ernst Schörner in Germany (who produced stereoscopic illustrations of intersecting 3-D shapes), from Federico Fink (a combinatorist in Buenos Aires), from Kobon Fujimura in Japan (check out Kobon triangles in his book *The Tokyo Puzzles* or on the internet) and from the polymath Lionel Penrose. Ruth and Judith recall that whenever he was in England, their father always tried to go to Cambridge to meet up with John Conway and others. They also remember Richard and Louise Guy being guests in the O'Beirne home, so too the biomathematician Cedric Smith and his wife Piri. Frustratingly, plans to meet Martin Gardner never came to fruition.

In 1963, O'Beirne translated Roland Sprague's *Recreation in Mathematics: Some Novel Problems* for Blackie. In a book review for the *Mathematical Gazette* at the time, A. P. Rollett wrote that 'the fact that T. H. O'Beirne felt able to undertake the translation from the original German is guarantee enough that the contents are mathematically stimulating and treated with originality' (Vol. 49, no. 368; May 1965). Of course, by 'felt able to' Rollett meant 'felt it to be of sufficient importance'. Five years later, O'Beirne edited Fred Schuh's *The Master Book of Mathematical Recreations* for Dover after it had been translated from Dutch. And at some time, a fine collection of puzzles collected by Rev. Henry Stanley Mercer, came into O'Beirne's ownership, a collection he duly donated to James Dalgety in 1974. Ruth and Judith recall being allowed to play with them carefully when they were young. The Mercer collection has been incorporated into *The Puzzle Museum*; check it out at www.puzzlemuseum.com.

Tom O'Beirne's book, *Puzzles and Paradoxes*, was published by Oxford University Press in 1965. It contains a 'rearranged and amplified collection of some of the articles ... in the periodical *New Scientist*.' Knowing of O'Beirne's connection with the founding of the SMC, I picked up a copy on the internet.

I was immediately taken by the comments on the nature of puzzles in the preface.

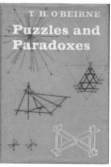

> 'An arbitrary multiplication of complications is not the best recipe for a puzzle, as we see it: puzzles and their solutions should rather derive a maximum of effect from an economy of means. Both can then have an aesthetic element — charm, elegance, beauty — which we wish to make apparent; but some of this is absent when solutions give no suggestion of how they could originally have been obtained.'

Those readers who are aware of Martin Gardner's books on recreational mathematics will not be surprised by what is in *Puzzles and Paradoxes*, but strangely the book does not contain the three ideas for which O'Beirne is now, perhaps, best remembered:

- an algorithm for finding the date of Easter
- polyiamonds
- O'Beirne's Cube.

Easter Sunday is defined as the first Sunday after the first full moon after the vernal equinox. Numerous complicated procedures have been developed for finding its date, including an algorithm Gauss devised using modular arithmetic. A simpler algorithm, valid for just the 20th and 21st centuries, was published by Tom O'Beirne in 1966 (O'Beirne, 1966). According to Martin Gardner, 'O'Beirne found he could memorize his procedure and as a party stunt give the date of Easter for any year during the relevant period by making all the calculations mentally' (Gardner, 1997, p. 238).

O'Beirne's algorithm has seven steps:

1. Call the year Y. Subtract 1900 from Y and call the difference N.
2. Divide N by 19. Call the remainder A.
3. Divide $(7A + 1)$ by 19. Ignore the remainder and call the quotient B.
4. Divide $(11A + 4 - B)$ by 29. Call the remainder M.
5. Divide N by 4. Ignore the remainder and call the quotient Q.
6. Divide $(N + Q + 31 - M)$ by 7. Call the remainder W.
7. The date of Easter is $25 - M - W$. If the result is positive, the month is April. If it is negative, the month is March, interpreting 0 as March 31, -1 as March 30, -2 as March 29 and so on to -9 for March 22.

As an example, let's see if we can find the date of Easter Sunday 2025.

1. $Y = 2025$, $N = 125$.
2. $125 \div 19 = 6$, remainder 11. $A = 11$.
3. $7A + 1 = 78$. $B = 4$.
4. $11A + 4 - B = 121 + 4 - 4 = 121$. $M = 5$.

5. $N \div 4 = 31$, remainder 1. $Q = 31$.
6. $N + Q + 31 - M = 125 + 31 + 31 - 5 = 182$.
   $182 \div 7 = 26$, remainder 0. $W = 0$.
7. Easter Sunday has value $25 - 5 - 0 = 20$, and will be on 20 April 2025.

Problem 1

(a) Find the date of Easter Sunday for each of the years 2030, 2062 and 2099.
(b) What was the date of Good Friday in 2019?

Polyiamonds are O'Beirne's response to Solomon Golomb's polyominoes. Of course, polyominoes, shapes made from sticking together squares, are commonly used in classrooms for enrichment. Pentominoes (with five squares stuck together) are particularly well-known, as are the tetrominoes that feature in the computer game *Tetris*. There are twelve different pentominoes and one of their properties is that they fit inside a 12 by 5 rectangle:

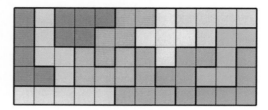

Sometime in 1959, O'Beirne simply asked himself the question, "What would happen if I replaced squares with equilateral triangles?" The twelve possible hexiamonds – shapes made from sticking together six equilateral triangles – are shown below.

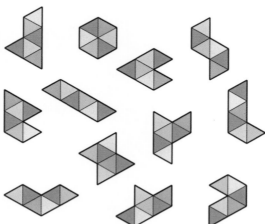

Richard Guy relates the story of O'Beirne's visit to the Guy family home in 1960 armed with a hexiamond puzzle. In short, "no one went to bed for about 48 hours." We may assume that the puzzle to which Guy was referring is one which is typically fashioned in wood, and still selling well today. At an elementary level, the object is to fit the blocks into the boundary shape; mathematicians seek all possible solutions.

Do all the hexiamonds tessellate? One that does, in a rather nice way is the shape referred to as the sphinx. Four of them can be arranged to produce a larger version of itself. And of course, four of the larger design can also be so arranged, ad infinitum.

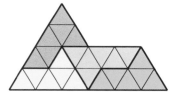

The polyiamond we know informally as a diamond is a rhombus made up of two equilateral triangles. In France the shape is known as a *calisson* because it somewhat resembles a confectionery of that name. Now there is a lovely result in elementary geometry about calissons. Imagine we are arranging

calissons of three colours (green, yellow and pink, say) into a hexagonal design, always placing them in these orientations:

Here are some hexagonal designs made from calissons:

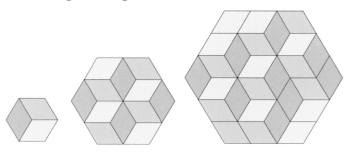

What do you notice about the number of green, yellow and pink calissons? Now explore different arrangements of calissons and different sizes of hexagon. Does what you've discovered still hold? Further information can be found in David & Tomei (1989).

Problem 2

Find all the pentiamonds and heptiamonds.

Finally, we come to what is probably O'Beirne's finest invention, a cube which can be split into components in numerous ways and then reassembled into other cuboids. Apparently, it was invented while considering the best design for standard boxes to fit optimally in a delivery lorry. Perhaps it is only eclipsed by the invention of the Soma Cube by Piet Hein, Pentominoes by Golomb and Ernö Rubik's wonderful cube. O'Beirne's units are $3 \times 4 \times 6$ bricks. It's rather obvious that $2 \times 3 \times 4 = 24$ of them would fit inside a cube of side 12. But what O'Beirne did was to stick the bricks together in fours. This gives the six components shown below, redrawn from the original article (O'Beirne, 1961).

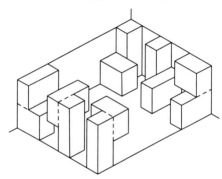

These components can be translated (i.e. moved without rotation) to make a closed cycle of six different cuboids as shown below, each move having two steps:

$$12 \times 12 \times 12 \to 8 \times 24 \times 9 \to 18 \times 8 \times 12$$
$$\to 16 \times 18 \times 6 \to 16 \times 12 \times 9 \to 12 \times 24 \times 6.$$

Here is one position in the cycle

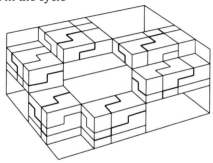

At the AIMS Center for Math and Science Education at Fresno Pacific University in California, students are asked by Dr Richard Thiessen to explore the potential of the 'O'Beirne Cube' for use with Fifth, Sixth and Seventh Grades (10-13 year olds). There are six pieces, each consisting of one long and two short (half-length) pieces stuck together, as shown alongside. So there is a nice question about the particular pieces, followed by the task of fitting them together to make a cube.

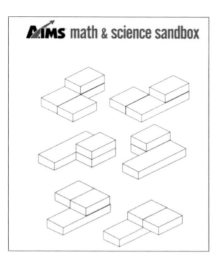

If you would like to explore O'Beirne's Cube further then check out

- the YouTube video at www.youtube.com/watch?v=fMIpy5-oMfo,
- the animation at www.puzzlemuseum.com/month/picm12/2012-02-obeirnes.htm
- an academic paper on the psychology of inventing packing puzzles, with reference to the O'Beirne Cube, at www.johnrausch.com/PuzzleWorld/art/art01.pdf

O'Beirne and the Scottish Mathematical Council

And so we come full circle. Having had a look at Tom O'Beirne's stellar contributions to mathematically-based electronic music and to recreational mathematics, we return to his involvement with the Scottish Mathematical Council.

Back in the 1960s, not only was O'Beirne a Fellow of the Institute of Physics, a Fellow of the Institute of Mathematics and Its Application and a Fellow of the British Computing Society, but he was active in these bodies, holding offices in all of them. He represented the Institute of Physics on the Scottish Education Department's Committee for National Certificate in Applied Physics from 1953 to 1956 and the Edinburgh Mathematical Society on the SED Committee for National Certificate in Mathematics from 1967 to 1970. By the time the Scottish Mathematical Council was being established in 1967, O'Beirne had considerable experience of industry and academe, he was actively involved in learned bodies and the SED, he was known to be a first-rate mentor, and had a reputation among teachers as a designer of ingenious problems and puzzles. Tom O'Beirne was a great all-rounder with his fingers in so many pies – knowledgeable, experienced and well-connected – the obvious choice as the new body's industry representative.

Answers

1 (a) Here are the calculations in tabular form:

Year Y	**2030**	**2062**	**2099**
N	130	162	199
A	16	10	9
B	5	3	3
M	1	24	13
Q	32	40	49
W	3	6	0
$25 - M - W$	21	−5	12
Easter Sunday	**21 April**	**26 March**	**12 April**

(b) In 2019, Easter Sunday is on 21 April, so Good Friday is on 19 April.

2   There are 4 different pentiamonds and 24 different heptiamonds. The heptiamonds are shown below.

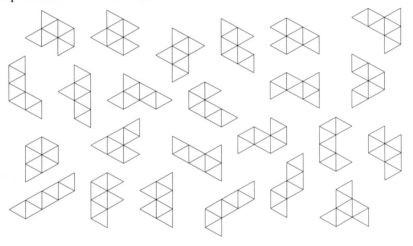

References

Butler, B. E., 'O'Beirne's cube and its origins', https://johnrausch.com/PuzzleWorld/art/art01.htm

David G. & Tomei, C. 'The problem of the calissons', *American Mathematical Monthly* 96, no. 5 (1989), pp. 429-431.

Frederickson, G. N. *Dissections Plane and Fancy*, CUP, 1997 (reprinted 2013).

Gardner, M. *The Last Recreations: Hydras, Eggs and Other Mathematical Mystifications*, MAA (1997).

O'Beirne, T. H. 'A six-block cycle for six step-cut pieces', *New Scientist* 224 (2 March 1997), pp. 560-561.

O'Beirne, T. H. 'The regularity of Easter', *Bulletin of the Institute of Mathematics and Its Applications,* Vol. 2, No. 2 (April 1966), pp. 46-49.

Finally in this chapter devoted to the SMC, a look at the Council's logo and a rather neat piece of elementary geometry arising from the fact that its components can be rearranged into a different shape.

1.5 The SMC logo dissection
SMC Journal 38 (2008), p. 33

The SMC logo consists of a regular octagon cut into four congruent pentagons and a square. The dissection is far from accidental. Not only can the five pieces be rearranged to make a square but the rearrangement is carried out by attaching hinges and swinging the pieces around, making it what's called a 'hinged dissection'.

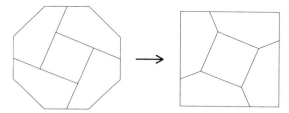

Start by rotating the logo 22½° anticlockwise about its centre.

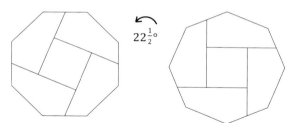

Identify the first hinge, H_1, cut along lines as necessary, and then rotate one pentagon through 180°.

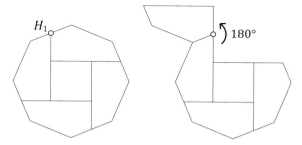

Identify a second hinge, H_2, make further cuts, and rotate two pentagons through 180°.

Chapter 1

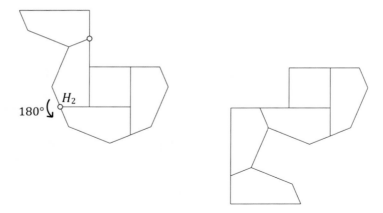

Locate the third hinge, H_3, and rotate a pentagon and the square through 180° to create a large square with a hole in it and a separate smaller square.

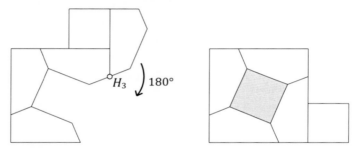

 Finally pop the small square into the hole, which it fits exactly, leaving just the larger square.

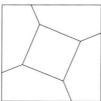

Incidentally, hinged dissections were first popularised in Henry Ernest Dudeney's book *Canterbury Tales* (1907), the most comprehensive treatment appearing relatively recently in books by Greg N Frederickson (*Dissections, Plane and Fancy*, CUP, 1997; *Hinged Dissections: Swinging & Twisting*, CUP, 2002; *Piano-Hinged Dissections: Time to Fold!*, A K Peters, 2006). Frederickson is a Professor of Computing Science at Purdue University in Indiana. Check out his homepage at: www.cs.purdue.edu/homes/gnf/.

2 Mathematics in Sound and Vision

Mathematics is created in the mind but usually not before information is received via the eye and the ear. Consequently, learners' understanding and progress are often determined by the quality of what they see and hear.

2.1 Mathematics and Language

2.1.1: Speaking figuratively
SMC Journal 43 (November 2013), pp. 68-72.

Day in and day out, I explain mathematics to other people, mainly teenagers via the spoken word, but also teachers and others through the medium of printed text, as here. The extent to which mathematics and language impinge on each other is quite considerable. Do they have the same domain, do they run in parallel or are there points of contact? This is the first part of an exploration of mathematics and language, from an initial plea that we set a good example when using language and correct pupils' poor English (or other language, where appropriate), to some ideas for enhancing mathematics in the classroom using various mathematics-language analogues.

It is now some time since *Curriculum for Excellence: Building the Curriculum 1* encouraged teachers to support language development:

> Competence and confidence in literacy, including competence in grammar, spelling and the spoken word, are essential for progress in all areas of the curriculum. Because of this, **all teachers** have responsibility for promoting language and literacy development. **Every teacher** in each area of the curriculum needs to find opportunities to encourage young people to explain their thinking, debate their ideas and read and write at a level which will help them to develop their language skills further.

The emphasis here is mine. Prior to this pronouncement, it was generally felt that mathematics teachers (and teachers of other subjects) would pay only passing attention to grammar, spelling and punctuation unless any failing on the part of the pupil impacted on the subject. For example, the correct spelling of mathematical terms should be actively encouraged by mathematics teachers. Quite correctly, the emphasis under *CfE* was for mathematics teachers to take a more active role in language.

The English language is in a state of flux and so it must be. All things must pass and all things must develop. The use of the latest technology has an influence and it's neither all bad nor particularly original. Having to pare language to the bone, youngsters are engaged in something akin to expressing mathematical relationships in symbols, IMHO. But it is far from novel, as demonstrated by this play on words from Scotland's greatest scientist, James Clerk Maxwell, to his friend Peter Guthrie Tait (in a letter of 1871):

R. U. AT 'OME?

On one level, it asks a question about Tait's whereabouts, yet it is really praising Tait for being all-knowing on the issue they were then debating.

Of course, for some time, we have drawn attention to the fact that the American media have a major effect on language in Britain. Some of the ways in which English is being mangled have become so commonplace that they go without thought or comment. Take, for example, the near loss of the word 'are' in favour of 'is', regardless of the number of things being discussed, the pronunciation of the verb 'to harass' where the emphasis should be on the first syllable, the use of 'obligated' rather than 'obliged', of 'stand-out' instead of 'outstanding', of counterclockwise instead of anticlockwise, and of calls by pupils (or is it 'students'?) to go to the 'restroom' or the 'bathroom'. On a slightly different issue, but most worryingly, because many British youngsters would dial 911 in an emergency, steps have been taken so that the call is immediately redirected to 999.

Enough of the moans, let us consider what we should be doing and what we might be doing.

Intonation and speech pattern

A teacher's intonation patterns are peculiar to that individual but reflect parental and regional influences. Whilst it is important that such variety exists, we need to ensure that not only is our delivery clear but that it is replete with tonal colour. A flat delivery is not simply boring for the class but suggests the teacher is not interested in the mathematics being delivered, a fatal flaw when it comes to generating interest among pupils.

As a contribution to multisensory learning, mathematics teachers can 'speak' algebra. This added dimension to what is being taken in by the eyes may make all the difference for some youngsters. For example, if pupils are struggling to understand the difference between $5x^2$ and $(5x)^2$, then enunciate the expressions leaving gaps in the delivery, as: "five ... x squared" and "five x ... squared", or alternatively as "five x squared" and 'five x all squared'. When teaching the distributive law, try writing $3(2t + 8) = 6t + 24$ on the board, standing to the side and, facing the class (the symbols out of sight), saying "three lots of two t plus eight is six t plus twenty-four". With practice, it's possible to deal with pairs of brackets such as, "two x plus three lots of six x minus one is two x lots of six x minus one plus three lots of six x minus one". (One or two jaws will drop!) Perhaps the teacher could speak such algebra (in dictation fashion) and the pupils could be asked to write it down.

Etymology and understanding concepts

Etymology is the study of the history and derivation of words. A grasp of the etymology of mathematical terms can help children to understand the concepts they represent. Here are seven examples that I use frequently with classes:

- *isosceles* is derived from the Greek for 'equal legs';
- *tangent* is from the Latin 'to touch' (we see it in the 'touching dance', the *tango*, and in *tangible*);

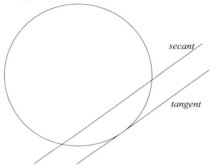

- *section*, as in cross-*section* and *bisection*, is from the Latin 'to cut' (to *section* something is to cut it up, a Caesarean *section* is a cut into the womb to release a baby): also a *secant* is a line slicing right through a curve, usually a circle;
- *surd* is the name given in ancient times to measurements that were 'absurd' or illogical, including the length of the hypotenuse of an isosceles right triangle (a multiple of $\sqrt{2}$); measurable lengths are quite the opposite, *rational* or logical;
- *perimeter* is the measurement around something (*peri-* is around in Greek, as in *periscope*, *meter* is to measure);
- *matrix* is from the Old French for womb (presumably because the entries are contained in those rounded brackets)
- *hypotenuse* is Greek for 'stretching under', suggesting a triangle in this configuration:

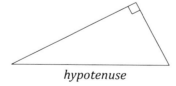

hypotenuse

Incidentally, ISOSCELES appears at the top of every list of misspelt words, both for frequency of misspelling and the number of variations.

There are many more mathematical terms to explore etymologically; so let the adventure begin! Two terms with an interesting cultural derivation are *algebra* and *algorithm*. Like many other words beginning with *al-* (such as *alcohol, alkali* and the *Alhambra*), they are Arabic in origin. In fact, the word *algorithm* comes from the name of the Baghdadi mathematician and astronomer Muhammad ibn Mūsā al-Khwārizmī, who lived around 800 CE. His most important mathematical work, *Hisāb al-jabr w'al-muqābala* contains the word *algebra* in its title and the main purpose to which al-Khwārizmī puts his algebra is the solution of quadratic equations.

Numerous mathematical words include *gon*, which comes from the Greek for a corner or angle. (Our word *knee* has the same origin.) There is *polygon* ('many angled') and several specific members of the family, from *pentagon* to *dodecagon*. The overwhelming majority of the number prefixes, *penta-*, *hexa-*, *hepta-*, *octa-*, *deca-*, *hendeca-* and *dodeca-* are Greek, making the polygon names pure Greek. Meanwhile, *triangle* is pure Latin. However, *nonagon* is problematic, in that it has one Latin and one Greek syllable. Purists insist on *enneagon* for a nine-sided polygon (both syllables being Greek), becoming quite uppity when they encounter *nonagon*. We should not forget *trigonometry*, which means 'three angle measurement', but that also leads us to other words that feature measurement in their etymology.

The derivations of the names of imperial units of measurement are interesting. An *inch*, being one-twelfth of a foot, comes from the Latin *uncia*, simply meaning a twelfth part. The *mile* started as the Roman's *mille passus* or 1000 paces. An *acre* is Old English for 'open field' or more specifically, the area of land ploughed by an ox in a single day. The *ton* comes from the *tun*, the beer cask of greatest capacity, suggesting that volume and capacity have gone hand-in-hand for many centuries.

Of course, these days, we use the *metric* system of measurement, which has the *metre* as its primary unit of length. We shall come to the sub-and super-units presently but not before alluding to *geometry* or 'earth measurement' and the circle's *diameter* which is found by 'measuring across'. Further examples include numerous scientific subdisciplines, such as *optometry* and *telemetry*, and of course, *perimeter*, already mentioned.

The SI prefixes used to multiply standard units by powers of 10 are rather interesting. Mathematics teachers use a small number of them frequently, whilst our science colleagues make use of a greater number of them:

Prefix	Power of 10	Prefix	Power of 10
deca-	1	*deci-*	-1
hecto-	2	*centi-*	-2
kilo-	3	*milli-*	-3
mega-	6	*micro-*	-6
giga-	9	*nano-*	-9
tera-	12	*pico-*	-12
peta-	15	*femto-*	-15
exa-	18	*atto-*	-18
zetta-	21	*zepto-*	-21
yotta-	24	*yocto-*	-24

All the prefixes used for the positive powers are Greek: *deca-*, *hecto-* and *kilo-* are simply Greek for 10, 100 and 1000; *mega-* and *giga-* are Greek for 'great' and 'giant'; *tera-* and *peta-* are effectively the Greek numbers *tetra* and *penta* with a letter dropped; *exa-* is a variant of *hexa-*, Greek for six, since $10^{18} = 1000^6$, *zetta-* and *yotta-* are derived from the Greek letter *zeta* and the Greek for eight, *okto*.

Meanwhile, the prefixes used for the negative powers begin in pure Latin but then wander elsewhere: *deci-*, *centi-* and *milli-* are Latin for 10, 100 and 1000, and *micro-* is Latin for 'small'; *nano-* is Greek for 'dwarf'; *pico-* is Spanish for a 'small amount', *femto-* and *atto-* come from the Danish *femten* (15) and *atten* (18) because they represent 10^{-15} and 10^{-18}, *zepto-* and *yocto-* come from the Latin for seven and the Greek for eight.

All this may be thought a little esoteric, but let me give an example of the use of one of the prefixes we use rarely in Britain, namely *hecto-*. In Sweden (and perhaps in many other countries for all I know), they use the *hectogram* rather than the *kilogram* for selling produce such as fresh fruit.

There are several mathematical terms with 'graph' or the etymologically equivalent 'gram' included. Graphs are themselves pictures or drawings, a parallelogram is a figure drawn using two pairs of parallel lines; a pictogram represents data by drawing in pictures whilst the histogram, given its name by the statistician Karl Pearson, is a diminutive of 'historical diagram'. I cannot leave the domain of statistical diagrams without mentioning the ogive. The name of this cumulative frequency curve is derived from the French augive which tells us that the correct pronunciation must be 'ojiv'. An augive or ogee is a term in architecture for the diagonal rib of a vault. On the left below we see crossing strainer arches in Wells Cathedral in classic ogee fashion and, on the right, the very first ogive, published by Francis Galton in 1874.

 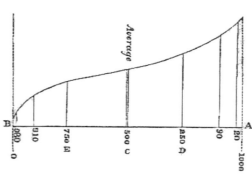

In both cases, the curve depicted is not the *ogive* we have today but the curve of its inverse and hence a reflection in a sloping line.

The word *lateral* comes from the Latin for 'side'. We see it in *equilateral* (having equal sides), *quadrilateral* (four-sided), *bilateral symmetry* (two-sided symmetry arising from reflection). Care should be taken when using *equilateral*

31

in geometry; it can be conflated with *equiangular* (having equal angles) and *regular* (effectively, having rotational symmetry). There is no ambiguity in the term *equilateral triangle* because *equiangularity* is also present. However, when it comes to other polygons, this is not the case. Here's an equiangular hexagon, produced by shaving an equilateral triangle:

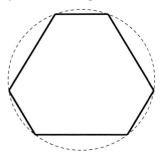

Ask your pupils if they can think of a quadrilateral that is *equilateral* but not *equiangular*, or one that is *equiangular* but not *equilateral*?

The language of countability

There was a news item in 2008 about signs in Tesco stores. In their attempt to fast-track customers with hand-baskets only, the supermarket chain had been using signs which read, "10 items or less". Though pressed to substitute the correct phrase, "10 items or fewer", Tesco opted to play safe and avoid confusion by changing to "Up to 10 items".

The issue here is related to the mathematical concept of countability. *Less* means 'not as much' while *fewer* means 'not as many'. So we should use *fewer* when referring to items that can be counted individually. By the same token, we should say *more* sand or a smaller amount of water but a *greater number* of buckets in which to carry them. Of course, care should be taken with the use of the symbols < and >, which are always read 'less than' and 'greater than', regardless of the countability or measurability of the stuff under consideration. And be aware that where we in mathematics depart from this general advice altogether, a computer's autocorrecting subroutine may well kick in, with *method of least squares* being 'corrected' to *method of fewest squares*.

Etymology of ordinals

Of the Greek ordinal prefixes we use only proto- and deutero- (as in prototype; deuterotype and Deuteronomy). In the main we use the Latin, the first two ordinals being the most fascinating. *Primus* means 'first' but is itself derived from *pre* (as in the *pre-* in prefix, i.e. meaning 'before'). *Secundus* means 'second' but it comes from the verb 'to follow', *sequor*. There is a sense then, that our *prime* or *primary* means 'before the second' and our *second* or *secondary* means 'after the first'. Clearly, our 'sequence' is also related to *sequor* and hence to 'second' and to 'sequel'; so it is really about numbers following one another.

Our word 'third' comes via early Germanic languages, by way of 'thrid' (which was more common than 'third' until about 400 years ago. The division of Yorkshire into 'ridings' or (th)ridings (third parts) follows the same route of language development.

Latin also has 'distributives', the first four relating to ordinals being *singuli*, *bini*, *terni*, and *quaterni*. They are retained in words such as 'single' and 'bicycle', in our number bases (binary, ternary and quaternary) and in the geological periods (Ternary and Quaternary).

Verbs (operators) and nouns (numbers)

Mathematics is a very exacting discipline, with little room for manoeuvre. If it were not so, the whole edifice would fall apart. (In some sense it did fall apart with Kurt Gödel's exposure of the circularity of Bertrand Russell's arguments, but let's not go there!) But in using the same symbol for a negative quantity and the operation of subtraction, we have created a looseness that impacts on learning mathematics. We might use a short, sharp hyphen, -, or even an elevated hyphen, ⁻, for a negative number, and possibly an 'en dash', –, to indicate subtraction, but it's all a little unsatisfactory.

However, there are parallels in language which might help here. We can stress that **numbers** are objects, linguistically **nouns**, whilst **subtracting** is an operation, linguistically a **verb**. Negative numbers are things, subtraction is something done to them. It is standard practice in Scottish schools to refer to a number such as -9 as 'negative nine', and this is far better than the commonly used 'minus nine' used by teachers in England (despite the latter being consistent with temperatures given in weather forecasts). Some teachers explain that (whole) numbers are staging posts (noun) on a number line and that subtracting is a movement (verb describing some action) in a particular direction between such numbers. It all ends up with soldiers marching up and down facing this way and that, but it can work well.

My preference is for negative numbers to be considered as debts (noun) and positive numbers as amounts of money in a pocket or purse. Subtraction becomes the process of 'removing' (verb). This gives me a sporting chance of persuading a class that subtracting a negative quantity is effectively adding. Referring to a particular member of the class, I say:

> *Imagine that John owes me £2. Being in a particularly generous frame of mind, I turn to him and say, "John, you know that £2 you owe me … just forget about it." At that moment, does he frown or does he smile? Yes, he smiles, and that can only be because his finances have improved; hence addition.*

Removing or cancelling a debt is advantageous to the debtor; subtracting a negative quantity is a positive move.

Pythagoras and his apostrophe

The apostrophe continues to have a hard time, misused by pupils and plenty of teachers. The standard way of teaching the possessive apostrophe is to divide its use into two cases. We have the *pupil's homework* if we are talking about the homework of one pupil, or the *pupils' homework* if we are talking about the homework of a whole group of pupils, $n \geq 2$. The third case, in which only the apostrophe is used in conjunction with the name, is rarely discussed. For us, the classic example is Pythagoras' Theorem.

Many names end with the letter 's', including that of Pythagoras. Where the person is someone from the far distant past, from ancient Greece, say, then just an apostrophe is used at the end of the name, but if it is someone from any other era and especially from the present or near past, an apostrophe and an extra 's' may be used. It's complicated, but let us at least get the spelling of Pythagoras' Theorem correct.

The structure of counting words

The way that different peoples count in their own languages is fascinating. Their number words reflect the base in which their system operates. In Scotland (for the most part), we use a base 10 system of counting (called *decimal* or *denary*) and that is signalled by the English words we use for our numbers. But there are other systems that pivot on 5 or 20, and some even stranger concoctions.

In our system, by and large, numbers above ten are given in terms of a number of tens plus a number below ten. For example, twenty-six means 'two tens and six' or $2 \times 10 + 6$. Of course, 11 and 12 are quirky in this system. *Eleven* is derived from the Germanic compound, *ainlif*, meaning 'one left' (after a group of ten has been removed). Similarly, *twelve* comes from *twalif* or two left over on removing ten. Equivalent words for 11 and 12 are seen in numerous languages influenced heavily by early German, including Danish and Lithuanian. In fact, Lithuanian is the only language which continues the 'left over' arrangement right through to 19.

Returning to number words in English, we must not forget the *dozen*, derived from the French *douzaine*, meaning a group of twelve and celebrated and retained for its overabundance of divisors. And then there's the *baker's dozen* of 13. The derivation of this term is sometimes explained in the following way. The baker would get into a rhythm of making loaves or rolls of the same size but this would often leave a small piece of the prepared dough and so a small extra one would be thrown in rather than waste it. Actually, the practice was not an act of munificence but a way of ensuring that the customer was not given 'short measures', the punishment in English Law (going back several centuries) being amputation of the very hand that proffered the unduly light goods.

To us, using a base 10 system may seem the only logical way to go about counting. There are numerous alternatives, however, with each revealing their base through the structure of their number words. A particularly unusual example is given on the next page. These counting words come from the Ndom language, spoken by perhaps a few hundred people on the Indonesian island of Palau Yos Sudarso. In their system, the main pivot is clearly at 6, with further pivots at 18 and 36; so it is a base 6 or *senary* system. Can you predict what 89 is in Ndom? (The answer is at the end of the chapter.)

1	*sas*
2	*thef*
3	*ithin*
4	*thonith*
5	*meregh*
6	*mer*
7	*mer abo sas*
8	*mer abo thef*
9	*mer abo ithin*
10	*mer abo thonith*
11	*mer abo meregh*
12	*mer an thef*
13	*mer an thef abo sas*
.	
18	*tondor*
.	
25	*tondor abo mer abo sas*
.	
36	*nif*
.	
77	*nif thef abo meregh*
.	

I have a soft spot for *vigesimal* systems in which counting is in twenties. There are vast tracts of the world in which such systems have flourished from Georgia to Bhutan, from Nigeria to the Celtic fringe of Europe, and from the ancient Mayan peoples of Central America to rustic, rural Albania.

Along the western margins of Europe, peoples have traditionally counted in twenties, from the Basque language of *Euskara*, through Breton, Welsh and Irish, right through to the *Scots Gaelic* of our Highlands and Islands. I was raised in Wales and learnt the vigesimal system on the left in the table below. It's a very quirky counting system, pivoting quite clearly on 20 but with minor pivots on 10 and 15 and that crazy 'two nines' for 18. In a push to promote the Welsh language in the 1960s and 1970s through Welsh medium nursery and primary schooling, a simpler decimal system was instituted (on the right in the table). Precisely the same process has taken place with Gaelic.

The French system of counting is part vigesimal, notably in the range 60 to 99, for example *quatre-vingts* (4 × 20) for 80. In the Middle Ages, counting in twenties extended to *dix-huit-vingts* ($18 \times 20 = 360$), especially in coastal regions where Celtic influences were strongest, but reform of the system into the decimal-vigesimal mish-mash it is today was instituted following the French Revolution. Interestingly, in Belgian French, *septante* and *nonante* are used for 70 and 90. This is also the case in Swiss French, where in addition, *huitante* is used for 80 in some cantons.

	Welsh (vigesimal)		Welsh (decimal)	
11	un ar ddeg	$1 + 10$	undeg un	$1 \times 10 + 1$
12	deuddeg	$2 + 10$	undeg dau	$1 \times 10 + 2$
13	tri ar ddeg	$3 + 10$	undeg tri	$1 \times 10 + 3$
14	pedwar ar ddeg	$4 + 10$	undeg pedwar	$1 \times 10 + 4$
15	pymtheg	$5 + 10$	undeg pump	$1 \times 10 + 5$
16	un ar bymtheg	$1 + (5 + 10)$	undeg chwech	$1 \times 10 + 6$
17	dau ar bymtheg	$2 + (5 + 10)$	undeg saith	$1 \times 10 + 7$
18	deunaw	2×9	undeg wyth	$1 \times 10 + 8$
19	pedwar ar bymtheg	$4 + (5 + 10)$	undeg naw	$1 \times 10 + 9$
20	ugain	20	dauddeg	2×10
21	un ar hugain	$1 + 20$	dauddeg un	$2 \times 10 + 1$
22	dau ar hugain	$2 + 20$	dauddeg dau	$2 \times 10 + 2$
23	tri ar hugain	$3 + 20$	dauddeg tri	$2 \times 10 + 3$
30	deg ar hugain	$10 + 20$	trideg	3×10
40	deugain	2×20	pedwardeg	4×10
50	hanner cant	$\frac{1}{2} \times 100$	pumdeg	5×10
60	trigain	3×20	chwedeg	6×10
70	deg a thrigain	$3 \times 20 + 10$	saithdeg	7×10

Counting in Welsh (then and now)

Finally, there is no more dogmatic vigesimal system than that used by the Danes. Up to 19, this system provides no surprises, pivoting on 10 as in many systems (with the exception of 11 and 12, as noted already). Twenty is *tyve*, and with no particular surprises for a vigesimal system, 40, 60 and 80 are effectively 2, 3 and 4 twenties. The quirkiness is to be found in between. For 50 we have *halvtreds*, meaning 'third half times twenty'; similarly 70 is *halvfjerdsindstyve*, which means 'fourth half times twenty' and 90 is *halvfemsindstyve* or 'fifth half times twenty'. The logic is that the first half is ½, the second half is 1½, the third half 2½ and so on. There are other vigesimal systems in which 90 is expressed as $4 \times 20 + 10$ but no other in which it is expressed as $4\frac{1}{2} \times 20$.

2.1.2: Parallel structures
SMC Journal 44 (November 2014), pp. 65-69.

In this part, we draw on parallels between mathematics and language. We begin by reversing the order of letters in a word and the digits in a number. Here, asymmetrical cases are termed 'reversals', with 'palindromes' and 'palindromic numbers' reserved for the symmetrical. We continue on through acronyms, and bacronyms to cryptarithms, snakes and ladders and anagrams.

Reversals

There are some words in English which, when reversed, turn into another word. Examples include: (animal, lamina), (desserts, stressed), (redraw, warder). In a sense, all numbers can be reversed to give other numbers, though we may frown at (2190, 0912) because, typically, we don't begin numbers with a zero. There are some interesting things that we can do by reversing numbers:

1. Take an arbitrary 2-digit number, reverse the digits to make a second number and take the smaller from the greater. The difference is a multiple of 9. Example: $74 - 47 = 27 = 9 \times 3$.

    The elementary number theory behind this property should be accessible to some pupils as soon as they understand that a two-digit number can be represented by $10a + b$ and its reverse by $10b + a$. Then, the difference is:

    $$10a + b - (10b + a) = 9a - 9b = 9(a - b).$$

2. Take an arbitrary 3-digit number, reverse the digits and subtract the smaller from the greater to get a multiple of 11. For example: $691–196 = 495 = 11 \times 45$. Try representing any 3-digit number by $100a + 10b + c$ and see if you can prove the result.

3. Explore what happens when a 4-digit number is used.

Is there an analogue in time. Reverse 19:07 to give 07:19. What is the time difference?

Palindromes

In language, a palindrome is a word, perhaps a phrase, which reads the same forwards and backwards. In 1948, Leigh Mercer captured the story of Ferdinand de Lesseps and his supervision of the cutting of the Panama Canal in this way:

A MAN A PLAN A CANAL PANAMA.

As palindromes go, that takes some beating!

There are opportunities here to embellish lessons on transformations, as palindromes have a reflective property. Of course, it is not the strict geometric reflection that also requires individual letters to be symmetrical, though words composed from the set of upper-case letters {A, H, I, M, O, T, U, V, W, X, Y} should provide such examples such as TOOT.

Numbers which read the same forwards and backwards are called palindromic numbers. So 16761 is palindromic but 387 is not. Here is a short investigation for the classroom: list and count the number of 1-digit, 2-digit and 3-digit palindromic numbers. (Answers are given at the end of the chapter.) For a larger task, try reaching palindromic numbers by reversing a number and adding the result to the original. For example, start with 69:

$$
\begin{array}{cccc}
69 & 165 & 726 & 1353 \\
+\,96 & +\,561 & +\,627 & +\,3531 \\
\hline
165 & 726 & 1353 & 4884
\end{array}
$$

A palindromic number has been arrived at after four steps. Is a palindromic number reached regardless of the seed used? The vast majority do so and in a small number of iterations, making the activity ideal for the classroom. But beware, 196 may be an exception.

Acronyms

Acronyms are formed by taking the initial letters of several words to make a new word. Surely it would be good to be a member of:

> **S**trathclyde
> **U**niversity
> **M**athematics
> **S**ociety

Mathematical acronyms are in very short supply. We tend to have the lesser form, the abbreviation instead: LCM, HCF, gcd, and so on.

Bacronyms

Bacronyms are reverse acronyms, taking the letters of one word as the initial letters of other words which define them. We might have:

> **A**ll   **A**ny   **T**welve,
> **L**egitimate   **R**educed   **E**leven, ...
> **G**eneralizations **C**ircuit   **N**ext?
> **E**ffectively
> **B**olstering
> **R**ational
> **A**rguments

Try your hand at inventing some, or better still, see if your pupils can do so.

Cryptarithmetic puzzles

A cryptarithmetic puzzle or cryptarithm is one which the digits of a sum (or other calculation) are hidden behind letters. Each different letter has a particular value, the object of the exercise being to reveal those values to establish the unique answer. Perhaps the most famous of them, and certainly the earliest, is this puzzle by Henry Dudeney,

```
  SEND
+ MORE
 MONEY
```

Here is the gist of a solution by Geoffrey Mott-Smith (1954):

M in the total must be 1, since the total of the column, S + M, cannot reach 20. If M is replaced by 1, the total in this column must be at least 10, so that the 1 can be carried. S must be 8 or 9 and, in either case, the letter O must stand for zero (0 or 1 would be possibilities were it not for the fact that 1 has already been used for M).

With O representing zero, column EO cannot exceed 9, and with no 1 to carry over from this column to SM, S = 9.

Since E + O gives N, and O is zero, N must be 1 greater than E and the column NR must total over 10; so E + 1 = N.

From the NR column we can derive the relationship: N + R + (+1) = E + 10. The (+1) is included at this point because we don't know whether there is a carry from column DE. We do know that 1 is carried from column NR to EO. Combining the two relationships gives: R + (+1) = 9.

Since we have already assigned the value 9 to S, R ≠ 9. So we make R = 8, and that determines that 1 is carried over from column DE.

Column DE must total at least 12, since Y cannot be 1 or zero. What values can we give D and E to reach this total? The only digits that are sufficiently great are 7 and 6, and 7 and 5. However, one of them has to be E, and N is 1 greater than E. Hence E = 5, N = 6 and D = 7. Then Y turns out to be 2, and the puzzle is completely solved:

```
  9567
 +1085
 10652
```

If you are hooked, check out Truman Collins's website:

www.tkcs-collins.com/truman/alphamet/alpha_solve.shtml

where there are cryptarithms for astronomers, artists and, of course, mathematicians, including ...

```
SATURN          MANET          COMPLEX
URANUS          MATISSE      + LAPLACE
NEPTUNE         MIRO           CALCULUS
+  PLUTO        MONET
PLANETS       + RENOIR
                ARTISTS
```

Collins even has a host of examples in what he calls the 'double-true genre', cryptarithms which are arithmetically correct, such as:

```
  ONE
THREE
+ FOUR
EIGHT
```

Word (Snakes and) Ladders

Word ladders were invented by Lewis Carroll on Christmas Day, 1877. Here are three with mathematical starting and finishing points:

LESS	**SOMA**	**HOUR**
LOSS	COMA	HOAR
LOSE	COME	HEAR
LORE	CORE	YEAR
MORE	CURE	WEAR
	CUBE	WEAK
		WEEK

Clearly, there are significant constraints on the construction of such sequences, not the least of which is word length. I suspect that changing TRIANGLE to its anagram INTEGRAL would be rather difficult!

Anagrams

When it comes to anagrams, mathematics teachers might enjoy noting that ELEVEN PLUS TWO is an anagram of TWELVE PLUS ONE, that as we always suspected, COMMITTEES COST ME TIME and, as A DECIMAL POINT once commented, I'M A DOT IN PLACE. If we want a pair of mathematical terms that are anagrams then we have TRIANGLE / INTEGRAL, though if we have trouble RELATING to them, then ALGORITHM / LOGARITHM also fit the bill. Worryingly for suriphobic mathematicians, MATRICES are all RATS and MICE.

Over a hundred mathematical anagrams and listed below. They can be used to fill the odd five minutes at the end of a lesson or held for an end-of-term activity. We have all seen some awful spellings of mathematical terms, so here's a way to reinforce not just the meaning of mathematical terms but their correct spelling as well. The anagrams are arranged into three age-and-stage groups – Group 1 (Primary), (Group 2) Lower Secondary and (Group 3) Upper Secondary. Of course, the Primary and Lower Secondary anagrams might be suitable for Lower Secondary and all three categories might be tackled by Upper Secondary.

Group 1

DAD	NECTAR GEL	FACTOR IN	SLICE CRIME
SQUEAL	LIKE METRO	DEAR MINER	RED QUAIL ALTAR
HARES	GLEAN	CLERIC	ATOMIC PILL UNIT
SMITE	THE GENIE	PRIME TREE	DIRE MEAT
USE MARE	OCCUR AT ALL	RECENT PAGE	TANGO PEN
EMIT	HANDOUTS	ECO SPASMS	TILER
NO BLOG	LIME	RICOTTA BUNS	REAL BAG
TIN EMU	MEDICAL	REAL TEQUILA	INTO SOUL
HEAPS	DECONS	RECENT TIME	BACKREST

Group 2

TRUE ROMAN	ANGER	REPAYMENT PLUS	QUILT RETAINER
HECTARE	DOMINANT ORE	EARTH RODENT	PATHOGEN
BRAINY	CLAIMED SPENT	CROATIAN PIPE	GIRL AMOK
MUTINOUS ALES	INCISED	MATURE ZIP	CANOPIED TIER
NOT QUITE	CARAT QUID	CAR EMPLOYMENT	SHORT MAGI
CITY VOLE	SIX OPENERS	MAGIC PORT	MOTORING TYRE
GO DANCE	MAIDEN	BARGE IN	BIBLIO PARTY
ANGLO AID	LOG PONY	CARROT PORT	CENTRE FOIL
ACE FURS	STEAL STEEL	BUSTS TUITION	ICONIC EFFECT
STATIC TAILS	TREADING	RODEO ANTICS	QUIT LARE
CALIPER PRUNED	MAIN BOIL	GREEN MANTLE	INSINCERE TOT

Group 3

COVERT	TOP RELAXATION	CAVE RAIN	LITERACY LION
OPEN NEXT	LEARN LOCI	ASCENT	ANOINT TIGER
LIMO TRAIN	ARMED INTENT	ALPINE OTTER	HEADED CONDOR
NOTCHED OAR	ANTI VIDEO	EXPEL NATION	ANTLER DENTS CAN
A MICROLIGHT	LATENT GAIN	QUIT CAR	RACOON HIDES
DUE MATING	CAIRN LOOTER	VAIN TRAIN	RECENT LAND ANTS
TO SCRIBE	MY TEAPOTS	LATITUDE	AFTER DEFINITION
ECCENTRIC RUM	TIGER NATION	CID REVENGE	LACRIMAL DEITY

We finish with some quotations which give terse insights to what mathematics is and what mathematicians do, and, to lighten the mood, a few jokes.

Quotations

Pure mathematics is, in its way, the poetry of logical ideas. ~Albert Einstein

Mathematics - the unshaken Foundation of Sciences, and the plentiful Fountain of Advantage to human affairs. ~Isaac Barrow

A mathematician is a device for turning coffee into theorems. ~Paul Erdös

Let us grant that the pursuit of mathematics is a divine madness of the human spirit, a refuge from the goading urgency of contingent happenings. ~Alfred North Whitehead

Music is the pleasure the human mind experiences from counting without being aware that it is counting. ~Gottfried Leibniz

Mathematics is the supreme judge; from its decisions there is no appeal. ~Tobias Dantzig

Can you do Division? Divide a loaf by a knife – what's the answer to *that*? ~Lewis Carroll, *Through the Looking Glass*

[T]he different branches of Arithmetic - Ambition, Distraction, Uglification, and Derision. ~Lewis Carroll

As far as the laws of mathematics refer to reality, they are not certain; and as far as they are certain, they do not refer to reality. ~Albert Einstein, *Sidelights on Relativity*

If there is a God, he's a great mathematician. ~Paul Dirac

The laws of nature are but the mathematical thoughts of God. ~Euclid

Life is good for only two things, discovering mathematics and teaching mathematics. *Siméon-Denis Poisson*

A mathematician, like a painter or poet, is a maker of patterns. If his patterns are more permanent than theirs, it is because they are made with ideas. *G. H. Hardy*

Mathematics is like a game played according to certain simple rules with meaningless marks on paper. *David Hilbert*

The only way to learn mathematics is to do mathematics. *Paul Halmos*

Jokes and witticisms

There are 10 types of people in this world: those who understand binary and those who don't. (Anon.)

A man has one hundred dollars and you leave him with two dollars. That's subtraction. ~Mae West

Arithmetic is being able to count up to twenty without taking off your shoes. *Mickey Mouse*

Old mathematicians never die; they just lose some of their functions. (Anon.)

Q: Why did the chicken cross the Möbius strip?
A: To get to the same side.

A physicist, a biologist and a mathematician are sitting in a café watching people entering and leaving the house opposite. They observe two people entering the house and, a little later, three people leaving the house. The physicist says, "The measurement wasn't accurate." The biologist says, "They must have reproduced." The mathematician says, "If one more person enters the house then it will be empty."

Answers

Ndom

In Ndom, 89 is *nif thef abo mer an thef abo meregh* (i.e. $36 \times 2 + 6 \times 2 + 5$).

Palindromic numbers (starting from 1)

The numbers 1-9 are palindromic as are 11, 22, 33, ..., 99.

The 3-digit palindromic numbers are:

$\{101, 111, 121, 131, 141, 151, 161, 171, 181, 191\}$

$\quad ... \{909, 919, 929, 939, 949, 959, 969, 979, 989, 999\}$

So the number of palindromic numbers with at most three digits is

$$9 + 9 + 9 \times 10 = 108.$$

Anagrams

Group 1

ADD	RECTANGLE	FRACTION	SEMICIRCLE
EQUALS	KILOMETRE	REMAINDER	QUADRILATERAL
SHARE	ANGLE	CIRCLE	MULTIPLICATION
TIMES	EIGHTEEN	PERIMETER	DIAMETER
MEASURE	CALCULATOR	PERCENTAGE	PENTAGON
TIME	THOUSAND	COMPASSES	LITRE
OBLONG	MILE	SUBTRACTION	ALGEBRA
MINUTE	DECIMAL	EQUILATERAL	SOLUTION
SHAPE	SECOND	CENTIMETRE	BRACKETS

Group 2

NUMERATOR	RANGE	SUPPLEMENTARY	INTERQUARTILE
TEACHER	DENOMINATOR	TETRAHEDRON	HEPTAGON
BINARY	DISPLACEMENT	APPRECIATION	KILOGRAM
SIMULTANEOUS	INDICES	TRAPEZIUM	DEPRECIATION
QUOTIENT	QUADRATIC	COMPLEMENTARY	HISTOGRAM
VELOCITY	EXPRESSIONS	PICTOGRAM	TRIGONOMETRY
DECAGON	MEDIAN	BEARING	PROBABILITY
DIAGONAL	POLYGON	PROTRACTOR	REFLECTION
SURFACE	TESSELLATE	SUBSTITUTION	COEFFICIENT
STATISTICAL	GRADIENT	COORDINATES	QUARTILE
PERPENDICULAR	BINOMIAL	ENLARGEMENT	INTERSECTION

Group 3

VECTOR	EXTRAPOLATION	VARIANCE	COLLINEARITY
EXPONENT	COLLINEAR	SECANT	INTEGRATION
TRINOMIAL	DETERMINANT	INTERPOLATE	DODECAHEDRON
OCTAHEDRON	DEVIATION	EXPONENTIAL	TRANSCENDENTAL
LOGARITHMIC	TANGENTIAL	QUARTIC	ICOSAHEDRON
MAGNITUDE	CORRELATION	INVARIANT	TRANSCENDENTAL
BISECTOR	ASYMPTOTE	ALTITUDE	DIFFERENTIATION
CIRCUMCENTRE	INTEGRATION	DIVERGENCE	DIAMETRICALLY

2.2 Visual Mathematics

[Taken from my Presidential Address to The Mathematical Association, 'Focus on the visual', Stratford-upon-Avon, 14 April 2022; published in *Mathematical Gazette* vol. 106, no. 567 (November 2022), pp. 386-399 and reprinted here with the kind permission of The Mathematical Association.]

Introduction

There are visual components of mathematics that are vital to the learning of the subject and should be a focus for its teaching. One aspect is the impressive capacity of the brain to visualise, an important element in the discovery process of some prominent mathematicians and scientists. We will look at the way in which the brain solves mathematical problems when confronted with an image and reflect on how, at least in English, we have equated seeing with

43

understanding. The pedagogical importance of diagrams in mathematics is then considered, with examples showing their role in problem-solving, elucidation, persuasion and decision making, and we will conclude with some particularly stimulating and revealing diagrams for use in the classroom.

Visualisation

Imagine being asked the following three questions:

- Can you play chess?
- Could you play three games simultaneously?
- Could you play chess blindfolded?

In many cases the answer to the first would be 'yes' and perhaps the response to the second would be 'I'd have a go' but, for the vast majority, the answer to the last would be either 'no' or 'perhaps for three or four moves'. Yet in 1783, François-André Philidor entered a famous chess club in London and played three opponents simultaneously whilst blindfolded, two of the opponents considered the best in London. He won two games and drew the third. Those who witnessed the contest were asked to sign affidavits to attest to the event's authenticity because the outcome beggared belief. As impressive as Philidor's feat was at the time, it has since been trumped and trumped again. In 2016, Timur Garayev played 48 games simultaneously whist blindfolded and riding an exercise bike. Over 23 hours he won 35 games, drew seven, lost just six and cycled the equivalent of 50 miles in the process.

We visualise either by interpreting what is seen (external visual thinking) or by pure creation (internal visual thinking). Spatial awareness arising from cognitive maps is controlled from the posterior hippocampus, tucked between the temporal and parietal lobes. Humans have the capacity to visualise in an exceptional way. A study of taxi drivers undertaken by the Wellcome Department of Cognitive Neurology at UCL in 2000 delivered staggering results. The research took place before the advent of SatNav and before the appearance of Uber, at a time when taxi drivers were tested on what they called 'The Knowledge'. Scans of their brains showed unusual physical development of the posterior part of the hippocampus. The volume of this part of the brain was roughly proportional to the number of years on the job (Maguire, 2000).

Many mathematicians have the capacity to picture two-dimensional geometrical diagrams in their minds, some to imagine and rotate three-dimensional figures. A few years ago, I was copied into an email from Douglas Hofstadter to Sir Michael Atiyah and, with the consent of both parties, it was published in *Mathematics in School* (Hofstadter, 2007). Hofstadter made reference to the Swiss geometer, Jacob Steiner (1796–1863), who:

> 'insisted on teaching all of his geometry classes literally in the dark ... He would cover all the windows of his room and would force his students to think in the dark'.

Hofstadter went on:

'teaching geometry in a pitch-dark room is a wonderful exercise both for teacher and for students, and it … forces one to ponder, 'What is visual imagery, if it is not seen by the eye?' It makes one realize that blind people have visual imagery every bit as rich as that of sighted people, and that indeed the eyes are just the entry channels for visual imagery for sighted people but that the actual imagery transcends vision and has to do with how space and shapes in space are represented in the brain.'

He tried to emulate Steiner by pulling down the blinds in his lecture theatre and working through Morley's theorem with his students in the dark. Morley's theorem states that if the angles of an arbitrary triangle are trisected, the rays produced intersect at points that define an equilateral triangle, creating symmetry out of asymmetry. The proof is far from straightforward and so it is not surprising that Hofstadter's experiment was not uniformly successful across the whole class.

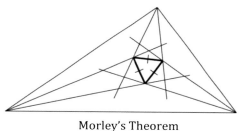

Morley's Theorem

Steiner is not alone amongst mathematicians and scientists in emphasising the importance of visualisation. The German organic chemist, August Kekulé first envisaged the ring structure of benzene as an ouroboros, a snake devouring its own tail. Lawrence Bragg, Nobel Laureate in physics in 1915, claimed his new ideas always came to him in the form of visual images. (In the quotes that follow, the emphases are mine.)

René Descartes wrote that

'**Imagination** will chiefly be of great use in solving a problem by several deductions, the results of which need to be coordinated after a complete enumeration. **Memory** is necessary to retain the data of the problem if we do not use them all from the beginning. We should risk forgetting them if the **image** of the objects under consideration were not constantly present to our mind and did not offer all of them to us at each instant.'

(Boutroux, 1900)

Albert Einstein commented that

'The psychical entities which seem to serve as elements in thought are certain signs and more or less clear **images** which can be "voluntarily" reproduced and combined … but taken from a psychological viewpoint, this combinatory play seems to be the essential feature in productive

45

thought — before there is any connection with logical construction in words or other kinds of signs which can be communicated to others.'

(Hadamard, 1945)

And in an interview with Melvyn Bragg, Sir Roger Penrose said that

'I was very much on the **visual** side ... other people could do it but it wasn't their primary way of thinking, the variation in the ways people thought about things was quite striking ... I thought about the subject [relativity] very much in **pictures** ... rather than equations.'

(Penrose, 2021)

Clearly, examples abound of mathematicians and scientists attesting to the impact of the visual on their thinking. But perhaps we should not be surprised. After all, the equating of *seeing* and *understanding* is embedded in the English language. The definition of

- **perception** is 'understanding fuelled by the senses, especially sight'
- **insight** is 'a clear, deep, and sometimes sudden understanding of a complicated problem'
- **clarity** is 'seeing in high definition or full understanding'.

Indeed, Sir Michael Atiyah in his 1982 Presidential Address to The Mathematical Association (Atiyah, 1982), argued that

'... the commonest way to indicate that you have understood an explanation is to say "I **see**". This indicates the **enormous power of vision** in mental processes, the way in which the brain can analyse and sift what the eye sees.'

The impact of diagrams

In a sense, the discussion thus far, is a preamble to the main arguments here about the importance and impact of diagrams in mathematics and elsewhere. So let's return to the brain itself and consider what happens when it is confronted with a diagram.

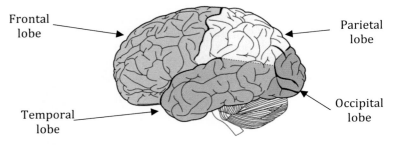

To simplify what are highly complex structures and very intricate processes, we can say that four lobes are immediately stimulated. The occipital lobe is the visual processing centre; here, the diagram is received. Instantaneous spatial

synthesis of the information occurs in the left parietal-occipital region. Meanwhile, the temporal lobe is supervising short-term memory and the frontal lobe is overseeing the whole process of planning, creating and problem-solving. And tucked inside, the hippocampus is handling spatial maps and orientations.

It seems to me that diagrams help to:

- present information in a concise and appealing way
- draw out the key features of a problem
- reveal the connections between pieces of information
- provide a setting for challenging or unusual problems
- support the explanation of conclusions

and, consequently, have the capacity to

- shape decisions, inform policy, persuade, and bring about change.

That contention comes from my teaching experience. Over time, I bagged a range of diagrams to support or clarify the explanation of a concept or to use in a particular example, and would pull them out as required. And when someone was stuck on a problem, I would routinely ask "Have you drawn a diagram?"– enough in itself on many an occasion to get that student back on track. 'Diagrams are essential' became a mantra for me and for my students.

It is reassuring that, over the years, mathematics educationalists have promoted the use of diagrams. In *How to Solve It*, George Pólya gave us a four-step plan to solving mathematical problems (Pólya, 1945). The first step concerns 'Understanding the Problem' and includes the key tactic: *Draw a figure*. Richard Skemp explained that when we draw a figure as an aid to problem-solving, 'by leaving out quite a lot of the visual properties of an object we can abstract at a higher level, while still representing the resulting concepts visually' (Skemp, 1971). Ideally, the diagram is pared to the bone, so that that only the essentials are retained and those that are not are discarded. He uses the figure below as an example, the aim being to calculate the height of a block of flats.

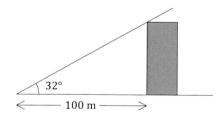

No doubt, teachers would be able to work backwards, suggesting the topic in which it might arise, noting the level of difficulty and assigning it to a particular age or stage. The question itself, or something akin to it, could easily be constructed from the diagram.

Diagrams that bring clarity

It is tempting to ask when diagrams were first used to bring elucidation but, of course, it is a question without a definitive answer. One early example was provided by that most prolific of mathematicians, Leonhard Euler. For part of his career Euler was employed by the Prussian 'enlightened despot', Frederick the Great and, beginning in 1760, he was charged with the science education of the king's niece, Princess Frederike Charlotte. Euler's lessons have been preserved in a series of letters to his pupil and among them we find his explanation of syllogisms (Euler, 1791 (1842); Musielak, undated). He gave the four primitive syllogisms in diagrammatic form:

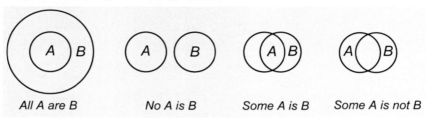

All A are B   No A is B   Some A is B   Some A is not B

While we now recognise the possibility for misinterpretation of such 'Euler diagrams' – hence their supersession by Venn, Carroll and Grünbaum diagrams – Euler's heuristics are clear. He believed at the time that any difficulty in understanding syllogisms could be overcome using 'these round figures, or rather spaces', writing that 'the mysteries of which we boast in logic and show with great difficulty, are immediately apparent by means of these figures.'

Diagrams that reduce complexity

The power of diagrams can also lie in their ability to convey a huge amount of information in a compact form, a classic example of which can be seen on the next page. Charles Joseph Minard's 'carte figurative' depicts the dramatic depletion of Napoleon's army during the Russian campaign of 1812–1813 (Friendly, undated; Friendly & Wainer, 2021). From crossing the Nemen into Russia from Poland in June 1812 with 442,000 men, the strength of Napoleon's army fell to just a quarter of that as it reached Moscow, with numbers declining further in retreat until only 10,000 survived to re-enter Poland.

The historian of visual graphics, Edward Tufte, commented that this diagram 'may be the best statistical graphic ever drawn' (Tufte, 2001). While we may be used to diagrams showing two or three variables, this one has no fewer than six. The **strength** of the army is shown by the width (thickness) of the line, the **direction** of travel is indicated by the diminishing thickness and the change from tan (advance on Moscow) to black (retreat), and the position (**latitude** and **longitude**), **time** and **temperature** are also indicated. It is a *tour de force*.

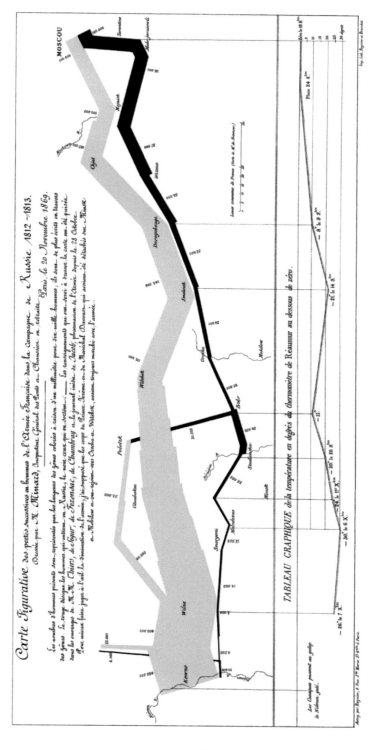

The Russian campaign as depicted in a *carte figurative* by Minard*

Diagrams that persuade

Concision can also be combined with elucidation to produce something which is persuasive, even to the point of effecting policy change. A case in point is Florence Nightingale's polar area graph. The story of Florence Nightingale has been told by numerous subject writers and biographers but more so in recent times by those with a focus on statistics as well as on nursing and hospital administration (Bostridge, 2020; Magnello, 2012). Her background was one of privilege, with social connections to politicians, including Sidney Herbert and her neighbour Lord Palmerston, the Minister at War and Prime Minister respectively during the Crimean War.

Nightingale's interest in nursing began with visits to hospitals in Italy when she was in her twenties. Later, with some basic training near Düsseldorf, an initial sortie into patient care at a small Harley Street establishment, a fairly generous annual stipend from her father and some experience at the Middlesex Hospital during the cholera outbreak in August 1854, she embarked on a path towards hospital administration. Perhaps it is fanciful to suggest that with such little experience her family friend and her neighbour would turn to her when news of heavy British losses began to emerge in what is modern-day Ukraine. Yet, not only did that happen but the judgement of Nightingale's parliamentary friends proved eminently sound.

Conflict between Russia and France broke out in Crimea in late 1853, with Britain being drawn into it a few months later. The British soldiers fought in nightmarish conditions – extreme temperatures, flies, scurvy, diarrhoea and cholera. The sick and injured were transported to Scutari (now Üsküdar), near Istanbul. The hospital was poorly equipped and a breeding ground for bacteria, and the treatment of the soldiers was badly organised. Herbert appointed Nightingale as Superintendent of Female Nurses in the East and she arrived in November 1854 with 38 nurses, just before the Balaklava and Inkerman casualties came in. Nightingale addressed the pressing issues of sanitation, hygiene and ventilation but also instituted rigorous record-keeping and data collection. She was already in contact with William Farr, who oversaw Britain's decennial census, and aware of his polar graph of cholera deaths.

The result of Nightingale's new hospital régime was a dramatic reduction in deaths at Scutari and she captured the before-and-after situation in a polar area graph which built on Farr's ideas. The full circle is divided into 30° sectors, one each for the twelve months to follow, their areas proportional to the deaths recorded, with the outer mid-grey shading representing preventable deaths. As our eye sweeps around the diagram clockwise from the '9 o'clock position' (the beginning of April 1854), the improving situation is plain to see.

The iconic graph appeared in Nightingale's *Health of the British Army* (1858) but it is not known whether she had drawn it prior to her audience in 1856 with Queen Victoria and perhaps more importantly the Queen's consort, Prince Albert who, as a youth had received lessons in statistics. It is tempting to imagine the Queen taking slices from twelve sponge cakes of different sizes (Victoria sponges, of course) and arranging them on a plate to dramatic effect.

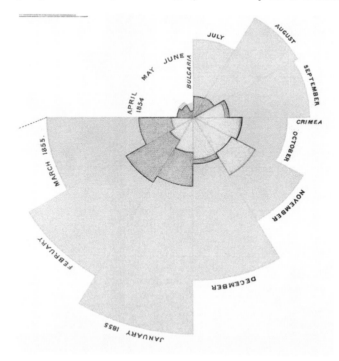

Anyway, with royal approval, with the support of her politician friends and armed with a wonderful diagram, Nightingale persuaded parliament to make organisational changes affecting the army and subsequently civilian hospitals, including an emphasis on accurate data collection and analysis.

Diagrams for posing problems

If diagrams are important in life outside the classroom, then they are equally important in lessons. For example, they can be used as vehicles for challenging and engaging geometrical problems. A style of problem advanced in my books on the elementary mathematics of area is characterised by questions such as,

'What fractions of the area of the outer circles are taken up by the quadrant and the sextant (sixth of a circle).

Becoming ever more popular are similar (yet subtly different) geometry problems created and disseminated by Catriona Agg and others via social media. They are typically drawn without any precision, making them attractive visually, but also demanding that solvers consider their assumptions carefully. The problem shown alongside is one of Catriona's.

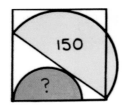

Diagrams and proof or demonstration

Justifying (or proving) key results in mathematics provides the subject's credibility and this is something that can hardly be overlooked by the teacher. Diagrams often enhance a proof or at the very least provide a *prima facie* case for its validity and hence acceptance. There are some particularly nice demonstrations that go under the heading 'proofs without words' and many of them have been collected by Roger Nelsen in three books published by the Mathematical Association of America (Nelsen, 1993; 2000; 2016). The following examples are taken from or adapted from Nelsen's compilations.

(1) Factorising a difference of squares and a difference of cubes

For the former identity, cut a square of side y from one corner of a square of side x to give the L-shaped diagram with area $x^2 - y^2$ on the left of the figure. Then slice off a rectangle as shown and rotate it into position on the right-hand side of the larger rectangle. The rectangle produced by reattaching it has base $x + y$, height $x - y$ and hence area $(x + y)(x - y)$. Since area is conserved in such moves, we have shown that $x^2 - y^2 = (x + y)(x - y)$. The standard difference of squares identity is thus established via the diagram.

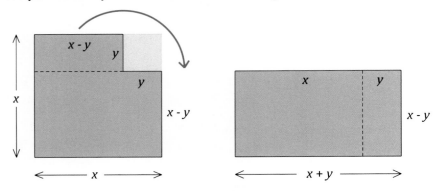

But there's more for the teacher here. The two pieces align on one side because they share a common side and the length of that side, $x - y$, is one of the factors of $x^2 - y^2$. Selecting where to cut is equivalent to identifying one of the factors. The geometry and the algebra go hand in glove, surely an aid to understanding.

And the approach can be extended to the difference of cubes. We begin with a small cube cut from the corner of a larger cube. Three cuts are made judiciously, so that the blocks created have one dimension in common (again $x - y$), and they are reconfigured into a prism.

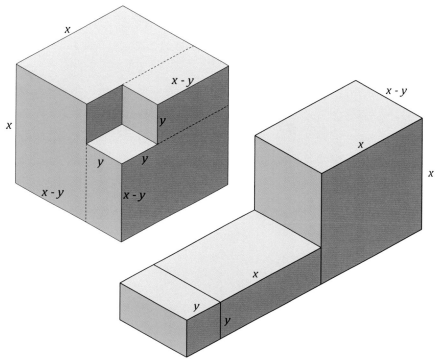

The volume of the original figure is $x^3 - y^3$ and that of the prism is $(x - y)(x^2 + xy + y^2)$.

(2) The sum of the first n squares.

Successive perfect squares can be represented by layers of unit cubes, each arranged in a square design. A sum of perfect squares can therefore be depicted as a stepped pyramid.

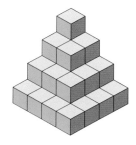

In the limited representation above, there are just four layers and so the number of unit cubes is

$$1^2 + 2^2 + 3^2 + 4^2 = 1 + 4 + 9 + 16 = 30.$$

But for the purposes of generalisation, we imagine that there are n layers. Take three such pyramids, as in the upper part of the figure below, rotate and reattach in a particular way, the blue one on the left joining the red one at base level, the yellow one on the right joining one unit up. This gives a block with an incomplete top layer; in fact, exactly half of the $(n + 1)$th layer is present.

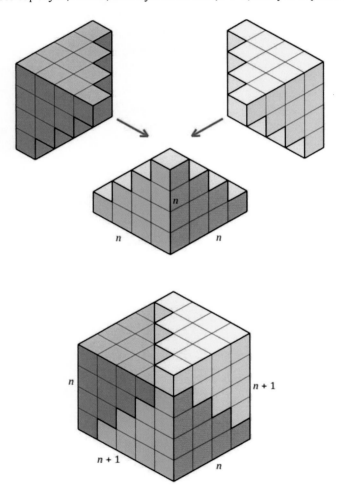

But if two such blocks are joined together – here I have rotated again for convenience – a cuboid of dimensions $n, n + 1$ and $2n + 1$ is created.

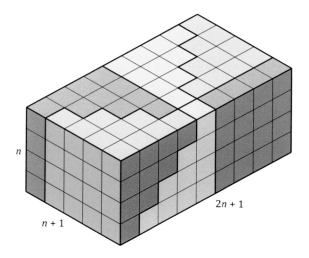

The volume of this cuboid is the product of these dimensions, but we must remember that this represents six times the sum of squares we require. Hence,

$$\sum_{r=1}^{n} r^2 = \frac{1}{6}n(n + 1)(2n + 1).$$

(3) The sum of the first n cubes.

Consider one 1×1 square, two 2×2 squares, three 3×3 squares and so on, as shown on the next page.

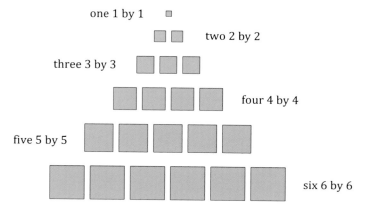

The three dimensions needed for cubes come about in a strange, some would say synthetic way. The side length comes in twice as if for area and the number of occurrences of each square size provides the third. Together these squares of different sizes and different numbers of sizes, fit together to make a set of asymmetrical steps, and four such sets of steps make a square.

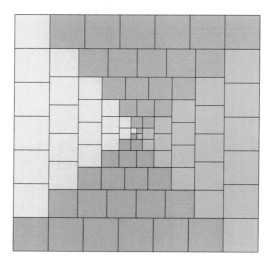

As in the earlier example, the representation is for a small number of terms (six here) but we imagine it extended to n terms. Paying particular attention to the bottom edge of the figure, it is made up of n lengths of magnitude n (below the red squares) and an extra length of magnitude n in the bottom right corner. So the base of the outer square has length $n(n + 1)$ and the square's area is $n^2(n + 1)^2$. But this is four times the required sum. Therefore, the sum of the first n perfect cubes is

$$\sum_{r=1}^{n} r^3 = \frac{1}{4}n^2(n + 1)^2.$$

Consistency of form

Among all the diagrams that are available to the mathematics teacher, those that exhibit a consistency of form are especially powerful. Here is a model that explains multiplication in arithmetic and in algebra whilst also helping to explain a key result in elementary calculus, the product rule. Note, in particular, how the partial products appear in the diagrams and in the written algorithms.

$$
\begin{aligned}
23 \times 17 &= (20 + 3)(10 + 7) \\
&= 20 \times 10 + 20 \times 7 + 3 \times 10 + 3 \times 7 \\
&= 200 + 140 + 30 + 21 \\
&= 391
\end{aligned}
$$

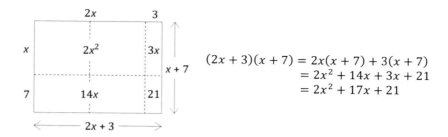

$$(2x + 3)(x + 7) = 2x(x + 7) + 3(x + 7)$$
$$= 2x^2 + 14x + 3x + 21$$
$$= 2x^2 + 17x + 21$$

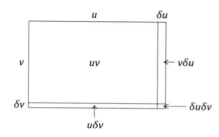

u is increased by a small amount δu
v is increased by a small amount δv

The derivative of *uv* is the increase in its area,
$$u\delta v + v\delta u$$
plus a vanishingly small quantity $\delta u \delta v$.

Avoiding disaster

Finally, a salutary lesson about what could go wrong should we completely ignore the visual. It was delivered by the British statistician, Frank Anscombe from his desk at Yale University in 1973 (Anscombe, 1973). With unusual dexterity, Anscombe produced four sets of bivariate data with very strange properties.

Set 1		Set 2		Set 3		Set 4	
x	*y*	*x*	*y*	*x*	*y*	*x*	*y*
10.0	8.04	10.0	9.14	10.0	7.46	8.0	6.58
8.0	6.95	8.0	8.14	8.0	6.77	8.0	5.76
13.0	7.58	13.0	8.74	13.0	12.74	8.0	7.71
9.0	8.81	9.0	8.77	9.0	7.11	8.0	8.84
11.0	8.33	11.0	9.26	11.0	7.81	8.0	8.47
14.0	9.96	14.0	8.10	14.0	8.84	8.0	7.04
6.0	7.24	6.0	6.13	6.0	6.08	8.0	5.25
4.0	4.26	4.0	3.10	4.0	5.39	19.0	12.50
12.0	10.84	12.0	9.13	12.0	8.15	8.0	5.56
7.0	4.82	7.0	7.26	7.0	6.42	8.0	7.91
5.0	5.68	5.0	4.74	5.0	5.73	8.0	6.89

The summary statistics for Set 1 are:
$n = 11$,
Mean of x values = 9,
Mean of y values = 7.5,
Sample variance of x = 11,
Sample variance of y = 4.125,
Correlation coefficient = 0.816,

Equation of regression line: $y = \frac{1}{2}x + 3$.

Amazingly, when the summary statistics for the other three sets are calculated, they come out the same in every detail. The lesson that Anscombe is teaching us is that these summary statistics hide the true nature of the data and that that true nature becomes apparent only through plotting the points. A diagram is essential to understanding what is going on.

The key is the appropriateness of adopting a linear model of regression or at least a particular linear model. A linear model appears totally justifiable for the first set (top-left) but for the second data set, represented top-right, the points lie on a parabola. A linear regression line is suitable for each of the other two sets, though as drawn here (and as calculated) a particular point has thrown things out. The outlier in Set 3 is dragging the gradient upwards, the outlier in Set 4 is masking the fact that the correct line is vertical, which would indicate independence.

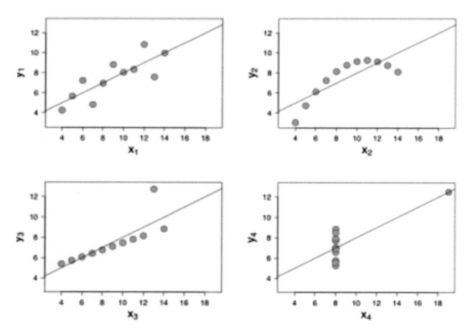

Anscombe's quartet of bivariate data

Summary and conclusion

In summary,

1. We have a great capacity for visualisation, and that capacity can be increased.
2. Visual stimuli and the images constructed in the brain are important in learning mathematics, especially in problem-solving. Pupils' understanding is bolstered by their own diagrams and by their teacher's diagrams, whether imagined or drawn by hand, whether static or dynamic, whether produced on a graphing calculator or in a software package, or in a spreadsheet, or by using an app.
3. There are advantages in having a consistency of visual models.
4. Diagrams are efficient in presenting information in a compact way and in an appealing way. They can be used to convince others of the accuracy of a result and make a valuable contribution to decision making at all levels.
5. The lack of a diagram can lead to a failure to make progress on a problem or, in the worst-case scenario, to the drawing of false conclusions.

If there is a lesson to be learnt, it is that we should focus on the visual.

References

Anscombe, F. J. 'Graphs in statistical analysis', *American Statistician* 27, 1 (1973), pp 17-21; online at

www.sjsu.edu/faculty/gerstman/StatPrimer/anscombe1973.pdf

Atiyah, M. 'What is geometry?' The 1982 Presidential Address, *Math. Gaz.,* 66 (October 1982), pp. 179-184.

Bostridge, M. *Florence Nightingale: The Woman and her Legend*, Penguin (200th Anniversary Edition, 2020).

Boutroux, P. *L'Imagination et les mathématiques selon Descartes*, Bibliothèque de la Faculté des Lettres de l'Université de Paris, No. 10. Paris: Alcan, 1900.

Euler, L. P. *Lettres à une Princesse d'Allemagne* (Partie II, Lettre XXXV, February 17, 1791, ed. Cournot (1842), pp. 412–417.

Friendly, M. 'The graphic works of Charles Joseph Minard' (catalogue of Minard's diagrams), online at www.datavis.ca/gallery/minbib.php.

Friendly, M. and Wainer, H. *A History of Data Visualization and Graphic Communication*, Harvard University Press, Cambridge, Mass., 2021.

Hadamard, J. *An Essay on the Psychology of Invention in the Mathematical Field*, Princeon University Press (1945) and Dover (1954).

Hofstadter, D. 'Thoughts on geometrical thinking', *Mathematics in School* 36, 4 (Sept. 2007), p. 27.

Magnello, E. M. 'Victorian statistical graphics and the iconography of Florence Nightingale's polar area graph', *BSHM Bulletin* 27, 1 (2012), pp. 13-37.

Maguire, A. et al 'Navigation-related structural change in the hippocampi of taxi drivers', *Proceedings of the National Academy of Sciences* 97, 8 (2000), pp. 4398-4403.

Mott-Smith, G. *Mathematical Puzzles for Beginners and Enthusiasts* Dover, 1954.

Musielak, D. E. 'Euler and the German princess', online at https://arxiv.org/ftp/arxiv/papers/1406/1406.7417.pdf

Nelsen, R. B. *Proofs Without Words: Exercises in Visual Thinking*, MAA 1993; also Vol II (2000) and Vol III (2016).

Penrose, R. (in conversation with Melvyn Bragg), 'Spacetime singularities', Oxford Mathematics Public Lecture (16 February 2021), available at www.youtube.com/watch?v=1zXC51o3EfI (especially from 1:29).

Pólya, G. *How to Solve It*, Princeton University Press, 1945.

Skemp, R. R. *The Psychology of Learning Mathematics*, Penguin, 1971.

Tufte, E. R. *The Visual Display of Quantitative Information*, Graphics Press, 2nd Ed., 2001.

3 Creating Mathematical Problems

3.1 Introduction

Solving problems lies at the heart of mathematics. It is where concepts, methods, routines and proofs come together, ideally with some novelty. Mathematical problems may be closed, those with a definitive answer (or perhaps no answer at all) so that when they have been tackled they are 'done'. Or, they may be open (or open-ended), so that as progress is made, avenues for further investigation open up at the same time. 'Problem solving' and 'Investigating' are terms commonly used for these two complementary mathematical activities and they are the subjects of this and the next chapter.

Presenting problems to students can only happen once you have either found them or created them. There are thousands of problems already written and in circulation in books and online, though, of course, they were created by someone, somewhere, sometime, and yes, teachers' time is valuable. But writing problems from scratch is a creative task that has benefits for the setter and the tackler, so perhaps it's time to become a bit more creative.

The one key characteristic of a mathematical problem is that there is a goal to be reached but no immediately obvious way to get there. It may be that the mathematical techniques required are in themselves routine but, 'which should be used and in which order?' This multistep requirement is a second key characteristic. The benefits to the learner of tackling problems are discussed thoroughly elsewhere. Here we simply suggest some ideas for the design of problems and provide some for you to analyse, acknowledging that, rather perversely, in doing so the need to create your own problems is reduced!

3.2 Creating problems: main considerations

When Maths Week Scotland was launched in 2017, the Deputy First Minister approached the Scottish Mathematical Council to provide seven problems for S2 pupils, one to be released in his name each day. About half the questions were taken from the Junior Division of Mathematical Challenge, which has an archive of past papers curated by the competition's national organiser, Bill Richardson, at www.wpr3.co.uk/MC-archive/index.html. As the Chair of the SMC at that time, and, I took it upon myself to supplement Bill's stock with some original problems and some adaptations.

A good problem is one which is pitched at a suitable level for the audience, is set in context (real or imaginary), perhaps with some quirkiness to grab attention, and which takes learning forward in a sometimes unspecifiable but qualitative way. The two examples below will help give a flavour of the creative process and the mathematical problems generated.

Example 1: Palindromic sales

In an effort to get people back into the company's shops, Bob Hannah, the owner of Universal Palindromes Unlimited (UPU for short) offered a WOW discount of 55% on all items, and then reduced the prices by a further £10.01.

Taking advantage of these discounts, Otto bought a piece of electronic gadgetry for £44.44. What would he have paid for it if neither of the discounts had been offered?

Solution

If the second discount had not been offered, the price would have been £44.44 + £10.01 = £54.45.

Since the WOW discount reduced prices to 45% of the full prices, £54.45 represents 45% of the full price of Otto's item.

So, full cost (without discounts) is $\dfrac{100}{45} \times £54.45 = £121$.

Comment

This problem is set in a realistic context, is quirky in the extreme, having five palindromes and three palindromic numbers in the problem itself and a further two palindromic numbers appearing in the solution. It is pitched appropriately, and there is some important mathematics to be learnt or practised, notably in working from 45% up to 100% of the price. Can you see how it could have been written? Incidentally, Chris Smith does a great job of explaining this problem at www.bbc.co.uk/bitesize/articles/zh8vydm#zfqrg7h.

Example 2: Currency exchange

A traveller plans a journey around four states, Abland, Ebland, Ibland and Ubland, returning to Abland at the end of his long walk.

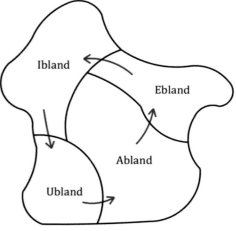

The currencies of the countries are, respectively, the Ab, Eb, Ib and Ub. There are no facilities for changing money at the borders. Instead a simple swap takes place.

- At the first border, the traveller swaps his Abs for Ebs at the rate of 5 Abs for every 4 Ebs.
- At the second border, he swaps his Ebs for Ibs at the rate of 8 Ebs for every 9 Ibs.
- At the third border, he swaps his Ibs for Ubs at the rate of 6 Ibs for every 5 Ubs.
- At the fourth border, he swaps his Ubs for Abs.

The hospitality of the peoples of these four countries is so wonderful that the traveller spends none of his money on his journey. What should the exchange rate be on the border between Ubland and Abland?

Solution

Imagine that the traveller starts with 100 Abs. In Ebland he has 80 Ebs, in Ibland he has 90 Ibs and in Ubland he has 75 Ubs. So 75 Ubs is worth the same as 100 Abs. Dividing through by 25 gives a simple form of the exchange rate: 3 Ubs for every 4 Abs.

Comment

Now the context is imaginary (some would say ludicrous) and the names of the countries straight out of an infant's fairy story, yet this adds colour. The problem requires a multistep solution, so the question about what to do and in what order is important. The mathematics is appropriate for age-and-stage, with a need to apply ratio and proportion skills.

3.3 The Daily Problems

Here are 25 of the Daily Problems created for Maths Week Scotland. The solutions are given at the end of the chapter but for many of them you will also find explanations inimitably delivered by Chris Smith at the Maths Week Scotland and BBC websites.

1. The inheritance

In August 2016, Eilidh wrote a will. She left her money to her 3 daughters, 7 grandchildren and 4 friends. Each friend would get £1,000, each grandchild four times as much, and each daughter four times as much again.

In August 2017, Eilidh made changes to her will. She still had the same amount of money, but sadly two of her elderly friends had recently died. Under the new terms of the will, each of her daughters would get only three times as much as each grandchild, and each grandchild would get only three times as much as each friend. How much did each daughter, grandchild and friend now stand to inherit?

2. Sums (almost) without adding

If the first ten positive whole numbers are added, the sum is 55. Check it for yourself!

Use this information to find quick ways to sum the:

a)   whole numbers from 11 to 20
b)   first ten even numbers
c)   first ten odd numbers
d)   first twenty whole numbers
e)   first twenty multiples of 3.

3. It's a knockout

a) 8 teams took part in a knockout tournament. Each match involved two teams, with the losing team being eliminated and the winning team going on to the next round. How many matches were there in the entire tournament?

b) How many matches would be needed if there were
    (i) 16 teams   (ii) 32 teams   (iii) 2024 teams?

4. The farmer's weight

Calum farms chickens and turkeys. One morning in December, he takes an egg for breakfast and then prepares one of his turkeys for the oven on Christmas Day.

Calum's weight is ten times that of the turkey and a thousand times that of the egg.

The turkey weighs 6930 g more than the egg.

What does Calum weigh?

5. Strikers

It was the 2023 season when Rovers won the league with that fabulous striking trio of McAnish, McBurnie and McClure scoring all the goals. How many did they score? Well,

> McAnish and McBurnie scored 48 between them,
> McBurnie and McClure scored 43 between them,
> McClure and McAnish scored 57 between them.

How many goals did the strikers score individually? Explain your answer carefully.

6. Sequences

(a) A simple sequence can be produced by starting with 3 and adding 4 each time:
$$3, \ 7, \ 11, \ 15, \ 19, \ ...$$
What do the first six numbers of this sequence add up to?

(b) For a different sequence, the first number is 5 and the sum of the first six numbers is 120.

What is the second number in the sequence?

7. Coins

Shamira has 60 coins and Dougie has 100 coins. Shamira gives Dougie a third of her coins and **then** he gives her a third of his coins. How many coins do they each have now?

8. Building blocks

These two figures have been built by sticking children's building blocks together. Now we can't see every feature or every part of these figures, so let's be clear;

- if we were to turn these shapes around they would look the same,
- the first figure is a lattice design; there are blocks on the inside,
- the second figure is an empty shell, with a cross-shaped hole in each face.

How many individual blocks were needed to make each of the figures?

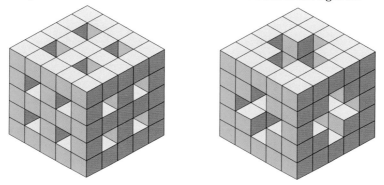

9. Weighing dogs

Here we have three breeds of dog: the dachshund, the poodle and the terrier.

A dachshund and a poodle weigh 11 kg:

65

A dachshund and a terrier weigh 15 kg:

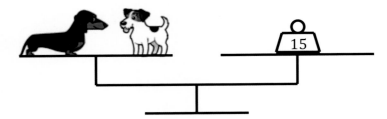

A poodle and a terrier weigh 10 kg:

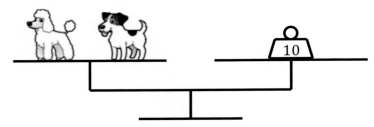

What is the weight of a dachshund?

10. Pentominoes

Designs in which five squares are stuck together are called 'pentominoes', and there are 12 different ones:

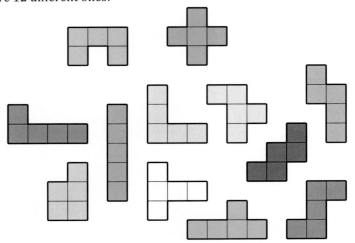

Show how the 12 pentominoes will fit together on a chess board with its corner squares removed. (The pieces can be turned around or flipped over if need be to make them fit.)

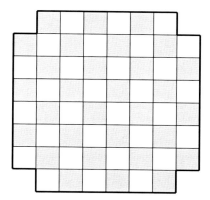

11. Stepped pyramids

This stepped pyramid has been built by young children and their teacher using some of the building blocks in the classroom. (The blocks are all cubes of the same size.)

(a) How many blocks would be needed to build it?

(b) Now imagine that the children want to build a similar structure with twice as many layers. How many blocks would be needed?

12. Squares and rectangles

a)   In the design below, how many squares (of all sizes) are there?

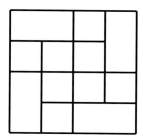

b)   How many rectangles are there?

13. Traffic calming

With the new 20 mph zones now in place, Rivka's journey to work takes longer than it used to. Now she can drive only half the distance at 30 mph, while the other half is at the reduced speed limit. What is her average speed over the whole journey to work and back home?

14. Fractions of a square

What fraction of each of the following squares is coloured blue?

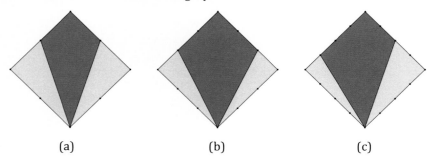

(a)   (b)   (c)

15. Painting the fence

A large, square enclosure was being painted. All the painters carried out their work at the same rate.

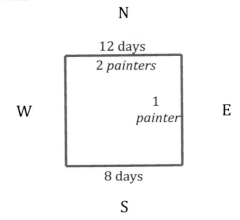

(a) Two painters took 12 days to paint the fence on the North side. Then one of them was called away just as they were about to paint the fence on the East and so the other had to work alone. After how many days did the painter finish the East fence?

(b) Then a team of painters was brought in to tackle the last two sides. The South fence was painted in 8 days. How many painters were there in the team?

(c) The number of painters changed again before the West fence was painted. If it took 50 days altogether to complete all four sides of the enclosure, how many painters worked on the West fence?

16. Number puzzle

I am thinking of three whole numbers. When I multiply the first two together, I get -6, and when I multiply the first and third I get -8. What do I get when I multiply together the second and third?

17. Triangle areas

Triangles *ABC* and *XYZ* are both equilateral. In each case, what fraction of the triangle is shaded?

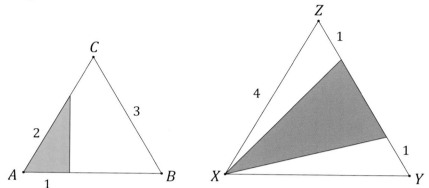

18. Edging the path

A square lawn of area 400 m² is surrounded by a path that is 2 m wide.

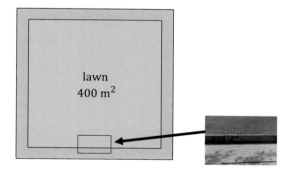

lawn
400 m²

Catriona and Blair need to put edging stones on **both** sides of the path to strengthen it. Each stone is 50 cm long and costs £12.

How much do Catriona and Blair have to pay for the edging stones?

19. Lottery win

A lottery win is shared among three people. Allan gets 20% more than Jane, and 25% more than Sinead. Jane's share is £3600. How much does Sinead receive?

20. Dotty rectangles

Here is a 6 × 3 rectangle drawn on dotty paper. There are 10 dots inside.

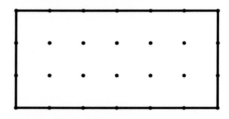

(a) How many dots would there be inside a 9 × 4 rectangle drawn on dotty paper?

(b) A rectangle with area 24 (square units) is drawn on dotty paper. How many dots could there be inside? (Note that there is more than one correct answer.)

(c) A rectangle is drawn on dotty paper so that its length is twice its width. Its perimeter is 54 (units). How many dots are there inside it?

21. A very long walk?

Before the Metric System was introduced, we measured lengths in the Imperial System, which was much more complicated. One of the units of that system, the mile, is still in use, but there were lots of units and some were connected like this:

        12 inches = 1 foot
        3 feet = 1 yard
        22 yards = 1 chain
        10 chains = 1 furlong
        8 furlongs = 1 mile

One day, Annie walked a distance of 316,800 inches. How far is that in miles?

(This question is much easier if you use a calculator. See if you can do it without.)

22. Powerful pyramid

$$2^1 = 2 = 2$$
$$2^2 = 2 \times 2 = 4$$
$$2^3 = 2 \times 2 \times 2 = 8$$
$$2^4 = 2 \times 2 \times 2 \times 2 = 16$$
$$2^5 = 2 \times 2 \times 2 \times 2 \times 2 = 32$$
$$2^6 = 2 \times 2 \times 2 \times 2 \times 2 \times 2 = 64$$
$$2^7 = 2 \times 2 \times 2 \times 2 \times 2 \times 2 \times 2 = 128$$

On the left of the pyramid we have what are called the powers of 2. The power itself (sometimes called an index) is the little number that is raised slightly. It tells us how many 2s we multiply together.

Now check out the final digits of the answers, shown in bold and answer this four-part question: what is the final digit of $2^8, 2^9, 2^{20}, 2^{111}$. Explain how you obtained your answers.

23. Keeping fit

During a pandemic lockdown, teenage twins Dan and Seonaidh take their exercise seriously. Each day, they leave home together to walk or run on the path that passes their house on an East-West line. Being twins they have the same speed of walking and the same speed of running as each other. Their running speed is exactly twice as fast as their walking speed.

a)   On Monday, Dan runs East for 8 minutes and sits down on a bench. Seonaidh runs West for 4 minutes. Then she turns around immediately and walks until she finds Dan still on the bench. How long does Seonaidh's **walk** take?

b)   On Tuesday, Dan runs East for 15 minutes while Seonaidh runs West for 15 minutes. Then Dan walks towards Seonaidh while Seonaidh runs towards Dan. How many minutes after turning around do they meet?

c)   On Wednesday, Dan walks East and Seonaidh runs East each for 6 minutes. Then Dan runs on in the same direction for 6 minutes while Seonaidh walks West for 6 minutes. Then they both turn around and run towards each other. After how many minutes do they meet?

24. Ways and means

(a)   The average (mean) of four numbers is 5. When two more numbers are included, the mean climbs to 6. If one of those extra numbers is 7, what is the other?

(b)   A set of three whole numbers has mean 9; a second set of four whole numbers has mean 16; a third set of five whole numbers has mean 25. If the three sets of numbers are put together, what is its mean?

(c)   Find two sets, each of five numbers, such that the mean of the first set is the median (middle value) of the second and the mean of the second is the median of the first.

25. Teachers' meeting

During the covid pandemic, some mathematics teachers had a 'hybrid' meeting. Two thirds of them were in the room and the rest were online.

After a tea break, four of the teachers did not return to the meeting room but an extra two joined the meeting online.

Then there were just as many online as in the room. How many teachers were in the room at the start of the meeting?

3.4 Creating problems: variation and extension

In a sense the problems seen above and the comments about creating them have a rather narrow focus. There are two ways in which we might consider extending the argument, though in doing so we will wander into some more complex mathematics. If a problem is adjusted to provide subtle differences from the original, then we might call that 'variation'. If on the other hand a problem is open to generalisation, then we term that 'extension'. In the latter category we find mathematical challenges that fall in that zone between problems and investigations. Examples of variation and extension follow here, though further discussion and problems of these types can also be found in Chapter 6 of my book *Focus on the Visual* (Mathematical Association, 2022).

Consider this design made up of squares of three sizes:

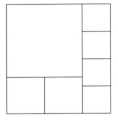

There are two obvious problems that could be set using this diagram. We could assign a unit length to the side of the largest square and ask for the side of the smallest square, or vice versa (a variant).

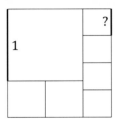 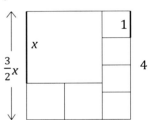

In the first case, the side of the intermediate square is ½, so the height of the outer frame is 1½ and the side of the smallest square is a quarter of that:

$$\frac{1}{4} \times \frac{3}{2} = \frac{3}{8}.$$

Of course, the result for the second case is 8/3, the reciprocal of the result we have already found for the first case. But if we were starting from scratch, we might let the side of the largest square be x, Then by considering the height of the outer frame as marked on the left-hand side and on the right-hand side, we could reach the equation

$$\frac{3}{2}x = 4,$$

from which the result follows immediately.

For further variation, we could use the same basic idea and tweak the problem again and again. When trying each of the eleven variations below, go from red to blue to find the ratio of the sides of those particular squares.

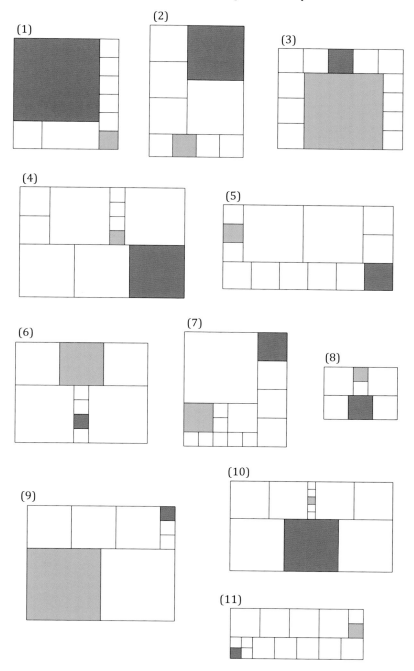

In a third variation, we have designs that feature only dominoes, i.e rectangles that are twice as long as they are wide. To ensure that they are not too difficult, the examples and problems here feature dominoes of four sizes at most. In this first example, the shorter side of the largest domino has unit length. So what is the longer side of the smallest domino?

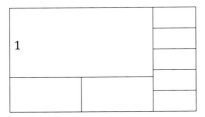

The outer rectangular frame of this figure has height 3/2 and this is subdivided into five parts on the right-hand side. So the shorter side of the smallest domino has length 3/10, and the longer side of the same domino has length 3/5.

Again, when trying each of these variations, go from red to blue to find the ratio of the sides of those particular dominoes.

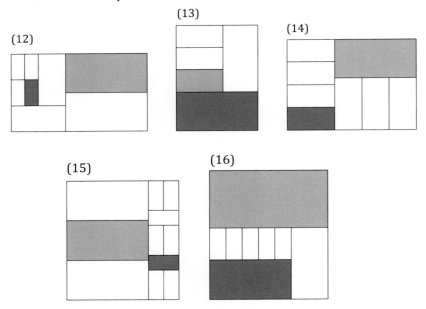

Here's another example of variation. In the figure at the top of the next page, the vertices of a square lie on the outer circle. Arcs centred on those vertices are drawn such that each touches its immediate neighbours. What fraction of the outer circle is coloured blue?

Solution: Draw the circle inscribed at the centre touching all four arcs and, without loss of generality, let it have unit radius. Let the radius of a blue circle be r; such a circle has AY as a diameter.

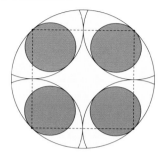

Now let's focus on just the bottom left part of the original figure.

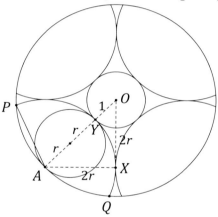

By Pythagoras' Theorem, $(2r + 1)^2 = 2(2r)^2 = 8r^2$.

The ratio of the radius of a blue circle to that of the outer circle is $r : 2r + 1$. Therefore, the ratio of the area of a blue circle to that of the outer circle is

$$r^2 : (2r + 1)^2 = r^2 : 8r^2 = 1 : 8.$$

The area of a blue circle is one-eighth of the area of the outer circle and so the four blue circles will occupy half the area of the outer circle.

And now for the variants: can you find the fraction of the outer circle occupied by the smaller coloured circles here?

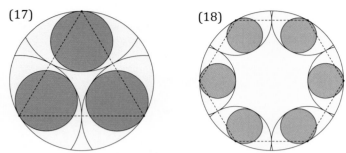

Finally, in this case, can you prove that the red circles occupy 5/8 of the outer circle?

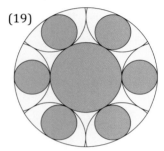

Let's turn to extension and generalisation. There's a rather nice extension problem among the Daily Problems from Maths Week Scotland. How many triangles are there in this figure? Explain your solution in detail.

There are two keys to getting a correct solution: first, notice that there are triangles of different sizes, not just individual unit triangles; second, don't miss the 'upside down' triangles.

The upright triangles are

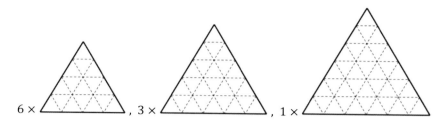

The 'upside down' triangles are

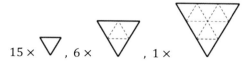

Total number of triangles = $(21 + 15 + 10 + 6 + 3 + 1) + (15 + 6 + 1) = 78$.

Extension: *Generalise to outer triangles of side n.*

The total number of triangles, T, is found by summing the number of upright triangles, labelled Δ, and the number of upside down triangles, labelled ∇ in the table below:

n	1	2	3	4	5	6	7	8
Δ	1	4	10	20	35	56	84	120
∇	0	1	3	7	13	22	34	50
T	1	5	13	27	48	78	118	170

There are separate formulas for n odd and n even, though reaching them is quite a challenge. They are:

$$T = \begin{cases} \dfrac{1}{8}(n + 1)(2n^2 + 3n - 1) & n \ odd \\ \dfrac{1}{8}n(n + 2)(2n + 1) & n \ even \end{cases}$$

Here's a problem for you that allows of extension.

(20) Pat places four dominoes in a 4×2 box, then does it again in a different way, and then in a different way again ... After a little while she realises that there are five ways it can be done. (Just think of a domino shape as a rectangle that is twice as long as it is wide, remembering that it can be turned around to be placed in the box.) Here are the five ways Pat found.

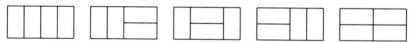

Pat wonders what would happen if she had six dominoes and fitted them into a 6×2 box. She managed to find all the possibilities. How many are there? Can you find them?

3.5 Solutions to the Daily Problems

1. The inheritance

We first need to find out how much money Eilidh will leave in her will. This is

$$4 \times £1,000 + 7 \times £4,000 + 3 \times £16,000 = £80,000.$$

Now under the new terms, let each friend get a single share. Then each grandchild will get three times as much, or 3 shares, and each daughter will get 3 lots of 3 shares = 9 shares. So the number of shares into which the legacy will be split is $2 \times 1 + 7 \times 3 + 3 \times 9 = 50$.

A single share will be worth $£80,000 \div 50 = £1,600$, which is what each friend gets.

Each grandchild gets $3 \times £1,600 = £4,800$, and each daughter gets $3 \times £4,800 = £14,400$.

2. Sums (almost) without adding

a) $11 + 12 + 13 + \cdots + 20$
    $= (1 + 10) + (2 + 10) + (3 + 10) + \cdots + (10 + 10)$
    $= 55 + 10 \times 10$
    $= 155.$
b) $2 + 4 + 6 + \cdots + 20 = 2 \times 1 + 2 \times 2 + 2 \times 3 + \cdots + 2 \times 10 = 2 \times 55 = 110.$
c) $1 + 3 + 5 + \cdots + 19 = (2 - 1) + (4 - 1) + (6 - 1) + \cdots + (20 - 1) = 110 - 10 = 100.$
d) $100 + 110 = 210.$
e) $210 \times 3 = 630.$

3. It's a knockout

a) With 8 teams, there would be 4 matches in the first round, 2 in the second round (semi-finals) and one in the third round (the final) making a total of **7** matches.

b) (i) With 16 teams, there would be 8 matches in the first round, 4 in the second, 2 in the third and 1 in the final round, making a total of **15** matches. Alternatively, we can simply observe that after the first round we have 8 teams and, from a), we know that 7 more matches are needed. Hence, we get $8 + 7 = $ **15** matches without further ado.

(ii) With 32 teams, the first round contains 16 matches after which we are down to 16 teams and so we require 15 more matches, by b)(i), giving a total of $16 + 15 = $ **31** matches.

(iii) The numbers 8, 16 and 32, all of which are powers of 2, are very convenient as no byes are needed. In contrast, 2017 is an awkward number and it would be tiresome to try to work out the number of byes. Fortunately, this is completely unnecessary if we look at the problem in another way.

Notice that in the cases of 8, 16 and 32, the number of matches is one less than the number of teams. This is always true, as we now show. Suppose we start with any number, n say, of teams. In the entire tournament, there is one eventual winner and every other team, of which there are $n - 1$, loses once (as a team is eliminated after it loses). Each match has one loser. Therefore, in order to have $n - 1$ losers, we need $n - 1$ matches. In particular, for 2024 teams we need **2023** matches.

4. The farmer's weight

If Calum's weight is ten times that of the turkey and a thousand times that of the egg, then the weight of the turkey is 100 times the weight of the egg. In other words, the weight of the egg is just 1% of the weight of the turkey.

But the turkey weighs 6930 g more than the egg, so 6930 g represents 99% of the turkey's weight.

The turkey's weight is $\dfrac{100}{99} \times 6930 = 7000$ g or 7 kg.

Calum weighs 10×7 kg $= 70$ kg.

5. Strikers

Let the number of goals scored by McAnish, McBurnie and McClure be a, b and c respectively. Then we can construct three equations from the statements given:

$$a + b \quad\;\; = 48$$
$$b + c = 43$$
$$a \quad\;\; + c = 57.$$

Add up everything on the left-hand side of the equals signs and do the same with the numbers on the right. This gives $2a + 2b + 2c = 148$, which means that $a + b + c = 74$. Compare this with the three equations in turn:

$$c = 74 - 48 = 26,$$
$$a = 74 - 43 = 31,$$
$$b = 74 - 57 = 17.$$

McAnish, McBurnie and McClure scored 31, 17 and 26 goals respectively.

6. Sequences

(a) The sixth number in the sequence is 23, so the sum is

$$3 + 7 + 11 + 15 + 19 + 23 = 78.$$

(b) (i) Solution by trial and improvement:

Let's try 8 as the second number; then the sequence is 5, 8, 11, 14, 17, 20, ... and the sum of these first six numbers is 75, which is too small by 45.

Let's try 13 as the second number; then the sequence is 5, 13, 21, 29, 37, 45, ... and the sum of these first six numbers is 150, which is too big by 30.

Let's try some number that's greater than 8 and smaller than 13, but closer to 13 than to 8, 11 say. Now the sequence is 5, 11, 17, 23, 29, 35, ... and these numbers do indeed have sum 120.

(ii) Algebraic solution:

If the first number is 5 and we call the amount we add on each time d, then the second number is $5 + d$, the third is $5 + d + d = 5 + 2d$, etc.

The sum of the six numbers is $5 + (5 + d) + (5 + 2d) + (5 + 3d) + (5 + 4d) + (5 + 5d) = 30 + 15d$. But we know that this sum is 120. So $30 + 15d = 120$ which has solution $d = 6$.

The second number in the sequence is $5 + d = 5 + 6 = 11$.

7. Coins

Step 1: a third of Samira's coins is 20 coins, so after Samira hands them to Dougie,

Samira has $60 - 20 = 40$ coins,

Dougie has $100 + 20 = 120$ coins.

Step 2: a third of Dougie's coins is 40 coins, so after Dougie hands them to Samira,

Dougie has $120 - 40 = 80$ coins,

Samira has $40 + 40 = 80$ coins.

They both have 80 coins.

8. Building blocks

The first figure has five layers. Counting from the bottom layer, the first, third and fifth layers all have 21 blocks in them. Both the second and fourth layers have just 9 blocks in them. So the number of blocks required is $(3 \times 21) + (2 \times 9) = 81$.

For the second figure, imagine that the crosses had not been punched out of each of the six faces. Then the figure would be a hollow shell, i.e. a cube with a big space inside. The top and bottom layers would have 25 blocks in them, while the other three layers would have 16 each. So the total number of blocks needed to make the shell is $(2 \times 25) + (3 \times 16) = 98$.

Now remove the crosses: there are 6 of them and each of them needs 5 blocks. So the number of blocks needed to make the second figure is $98 - 30 = 68$.

9. Weighing dogs

From the second and third diagrams, we can see that a dachshund weighs 5 kg more than a poodle.

The first diagram shows that a dachshund and a poodle weigh 11 kg together.

So we need two weights such that when we add them we get 11 kg and when we take the smaller from the larger we get 5 kg. This leads almost directly to the conclusion that the dachshund weighs 8 kg (and the poodle weighs 3 kg).

Here's an alternative way of doing the problem using the scales. The diagrams below show all three sets of scales (the third having been turned around).

Now pile everything from the left-hand pans onto a single pan, and everything on the right-hand pans onto a single pan. Then we have:

Now take a terrier, a poodle and 10kg from each side:

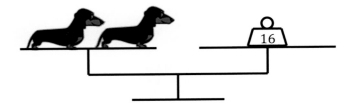

and the result follows immediately.

10. Pentominoes

Here's one solution. There are associated solutions arising from rotations and reflections of this one, and there may be others which are intrinsically different.

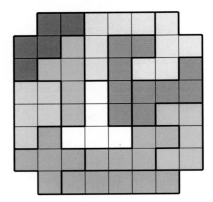

11. Stepped pyramids

(a) The pink layer on top has a single block.
The yellow layer has 5 blocks (one of which is hidden under the red block).
The blue layer has $1 + 3 + 5 + 3 + 1 = 13$ blocks.

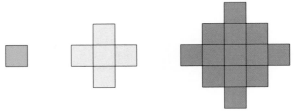

Total number of blocks in the 3 layers of the pyramid is $1 + 5 + 13 = 19$.

(b) Layers 4, 5 and 6 (working downwards) will have the following numbers of blocks in them:
$$1 + 3 + 5 + 7 + 5 + 3 + 1 = 25,$$
$$1 + 3 + 5 + 7 + 9 + 7 + 5 + 3 + 1 = 41,$$
$$1 + 3 + 5 + 7 + 9 + 11 + 9 + 7 + 5 + 3 + 1 = 61.$$

The 6-layer stepped pyramid has $1 + 5 + 13 + 25 + 41 + 61 = 146$ blocks.

12. Squares and rectangles

There are 8 squares of side 1, 5 squares of side 2 and 1 square of side 4: total 14.

In addition, there are:
- 6 rectangles of length 2 and width 1, and another 6 rectangles of length 1 and width 2;
- 4 rectangles of length 3 and width 1, and another 4 rectangles of length 1 and width 3;
- 2 rectangles of length 3 and width 2, and another 2 rectangles of length 2 and width 3;
- 2 rectangles of length 4 and width 2, and another 2 rectangles of length 2 and width 4.

So the total number of rectangles is $14 + 2(6 + 4 + 2 + 2) = 14 + 2 \times 14 = 42$.

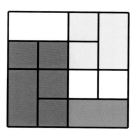 The diagram alongside shows an example of each of a square of side 2 (yellow), a rectangle of length 2 and width 1 (red) and a rectangle of length 2 and width 3 (blue).

13. Traffic calming

This problem is sometimes considered a trick question because the 'obvious' answer of 25 mph is wrong. Since

$$\text{(average) speed} = \frac{\text{(total) distance}}{\text{(total) time}},$$

it can only be solved by making use of the distance between Rivka's home and her workplace and calculating the time taken for the parts of the journey undertaken at 30 mph and those at 20 mph separately and then together. That distance is not stated and yet strangely it doesn't affect the answer.

Since any distance will do, let's say it's exactly 20 miles between Rivka's home and her work, so that she does 10 miles at 30 mph and 10 miles at 20 mph.

Time taken to travel 10 miles at 30 mph $= \frac{1}{3}$ hour $= 20$ minutes.

Time taken to travel 10 miles at 20 mph $= \frac{1}{2}$ hour $= 30$ minutes.

So, overall, Rivka has travelled 20 miles in 50 minutes, which is the same average speed as 4 miles in 10 minutes or 24 mph.

(If you are not convinced that the answer is the same for all possible journeys, try some other distances to Rivka's workplace, such as 6 miles or 10 miles.)

14. Fractions of a square

Let the squares have unit area and assume that the points marked divide the sides into halves, thirds and quarters respectively. Here are visual solutions for the first two parts, found by first rearranging the yellow triangles. The blue rectangles must be equal in area to the regions coloured blue in the original diagrams, so the answers are ½ and ⅔, respectively.

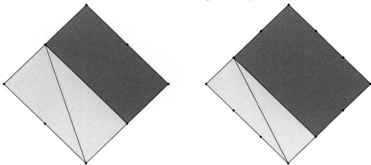

The last part is more troublesome but if we rearrange the pieces as shown below, the yellow triangles have areas of 1/8 and 1/4. Remembering that 1/4 is the same as 2/8, the total area coloured yellow is 3/8. So the area coloured blue is 5/8.

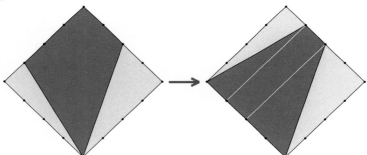

15. Painting the fence

(a) A painter working alone takes twice as long as two painters working together. So it took 24 days to paint the East fence.
(b) Eight days is 1/3 of the time that a single painter took so there must have been 3 painters.
(c) The time taken to paint the first three sides was $12 + 24 + 8 = 44$ days. If it took 50 days altogether, then the West fence was painted in 6 days. If it takes 24 days for one painter to complete a fence, then it took 6 days to complete if there were 4 painters.

16. Number puzzle

Let the three numbers be a, b and c.

If $ab = -6$, then there are four possibilities:
$$(1, -6, c), (-1, 6, c), (2, -3, c), (-2, 3, c).$$

If $ac = -8$, then there are four possibilities:
$$(1, b, -8), (-1, b, 8), (2, b, -4), (-2, b, 4).$$

Putting these together we have: $(1, -6, -8), (-1, 6, 8), (2, -3, -4), (-2, 3, 4)$.

From the first two solutions we get $bc = 48$, and from the last two, $bc = 12$.

17. Triangle areas

The fraction coloured red can be found easily by dividing ABC into nine smaller equilateral triangles. One of those small triangles and two half triangles are coloured, i.e. the equivalent of two small triangles are coloured (out of nine). So the fraction coloured red is 2/9.

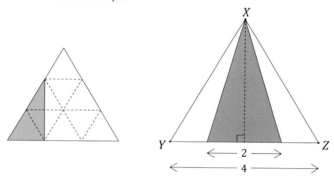

Now, for convenience, we turn XYZ into the position shown above. The outer triangle and the triangle coloured blue have the same height but the base of the blue triangle is only half as great as the base of XYZ. So the fraction coloured blue is 1/2.

18. Edging the path

If the lawn is square and has area 400 square metres then its side is 20 m. So the inside edging stones have total length 80 m.

If the path is 2 m wide, then the outer edge of the path has length 24 m on each side, i.e. 96 m.

So the total length to be edged is 176 m.

Since the edging stones have length ½m, $2 \times 176 = 352$ stones are needed.

Cost = $352 \times £12 = £4224$.

19. Lottery win

Jane gets £3600 and Allan gets 20% more than her.

So Allan gets .£3600 + £720 = £4320.

Allan gets 25% more than Sinead, so Sinead gets 4/5 of Allan's amount. Now, 1/5 of Allan's amount is £4320 ÷ 5 = £864.

Therefore, Sinead gets 4 × £864 = £3456.

20. Dotty rectangles

(a) A 9 × 4 rectangle would have 24 dots inside (arranged in an 8 by 3 pattern).

(b) The dimensions of the rectangle could be 24 × 1, 12 × 2, 8 × 3 or 6 × 4. So the possible numbers of dots inside are 0, 11, 14, 15.

(c) If the perimeter is 54, then length + width = 27. Sharing 27 so that one number is twice the other gives 18 and 9. So the length is 18 and the width is 9. Therefore, the number of dots inside is 17 × 8 = 136.

21. A very long walk?

This question is all about dividing. Divide by 12, then 3, then 22, then 10 and finally 8.

316,800 inches = 26,400 feet = 8,800 yards = 400 chains = 40 furlongs = 5 miles.

22. Powerful pyramid

The final digits repeat the pattern 2, 4, 8, 6 endlessly. So the first two answers are straightforward:

2^8 finishes with a **6** and 2^9 finishes with a **2**. The actual values of these powers of 2 can be found simply by doubling 128 to give 25**6** and then doubling again to give 51**2**. For the third answer, we might notice that if the power is a multiple of 4 (such as 4, 8, 12, 16, 20, 24), then the final digit is always **6**. 112 is a multiple of 4, so the final digit of 2^{112} is 6. Therefore, the final digit of 2^{111} is **8**.

23. Keeping fit

a) Convert everything to walking pace. Dan reaches the bench after 16 minutes. Seonaidh walks away from Dan for 4 minutes and then back to where she started and on beyond towards the bench, taking a further 4 + 16 = 20 minutes. So she walks for a total of 24 minutes.

b) After 15 minutes, Dan and Seonaidh are 30 minutes apart at running pace, an hour apart at walking pace. So they will meet after a further 20 minutes during which time Dan has walked for 20 minutes and Seonaidh has covered the equivalent of 40 minutes at walking pace.

c) Convert everything to running pace. Seonaidh runs 6 minutes East and then walks 6 minutes West, but the walk is equivalent to a 3-minute run, so she is now 3 minutes East of her starting position, at running pace. Meanwhile, Dan initially walks East for 6 minutes which is equivalent to 3 minutes at running pace, and then runs for a further 6 minutes in the same direction. So he is now 9 minutes East of his starting position at running pace. So they are now 6 minutes apart as they start running towards each other. They meet after 3 minutes.

24. Ways and means

(a) The sum of the four original numbers is $5 \times 4 = 20$. With two additional numbers the sum is $7 \times 6 = 42$. So the additional numbers add to $42 - 20 = 22$. If one of them is 7 then the other is 15.

(b) The total of all the numbers is $3 \times 9 + 4 \times 16 + 5 \times 25 = 27 + 64 + 125 = 216$. There are 12 numbers altogether, so the mean is $216 \div 12 = 18$.

(c) There are numerous possibilities. For example the sets $\{1, 3, 6, 7, 8\}$ and $\{2, 4, 5, 8, 11\}$ are such that the mean of the first and the median of the second are both 5, while the median of the first and the mean of the second are both 6.

25. Teachers' meeting

Let n be the total number of teachers at the start of the meeting. The number who were in the room is $\frac{2}{3}n$ and the number online was $\frac{1}{3}n$.

After the tea break, the number who were in the room is $\frac{2}{3}n - 4$ and the number online was $\frac{1}{3}n + 2$. Since these numbers are equal,

$$\frac{2}{3}n - 4 = \frac{1}{3}n + 2$$
$$\frac{1}{3}n = 6$$
$$n = 18.$$

There were 18 teachers altogether at the start, 12 of them in the room.

This problem could also be solved by trial and improvement, perhaps starting with 20 in the room, 10 online; then adjusting the numbers accordingly until the correct solution emerges. Of course the algebraic approach or something akin to it without the symbols is more general and hence more powerful.

3.6 Solutions to the variation and extension problems

Here are some skeleton solutions for the problems involving squares. They should be sufficient for the following ratios of side lengths to be determined:

(1) $2 : 9$ (2) $5 : 12$ (3) $60 : 19$ (4) $3 : 11$ (5) $12 : 17$ (6) $1 : 3$ (7) $1 : 1$ (8) $3 : 5$ (9) $5 : 1$ (10) $1 : 7$ (11) $3 : 4$

(1)

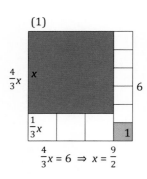

$\frac{4}{3}x = 6 \implies x = \frac{9}{2}$

(2)

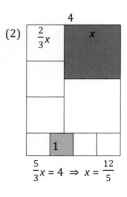

$\frac{5}{3}x = 4 \implies x = \frac{12}{5}$

(3)

$1 + \frac{1}{3} + \frac{1}{4} = \frac{19}{12}$

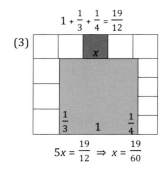

$5x = \frac{19}{12} \implies x = \frac{19}{60}$

(4)

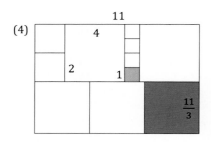

(5)

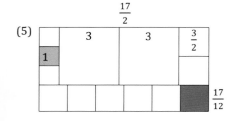

(6)

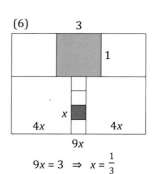

$9x = 3 \implies x = \frac{1}{3}$

(7)

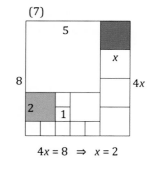

$4x = 8 \implies x = 2$

(8)

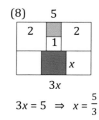

$3x = 5 \implies x = \frac{5}{3}$

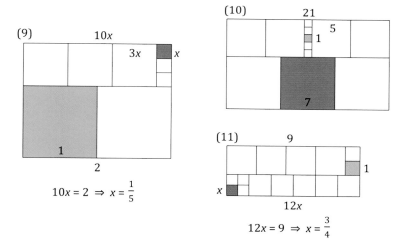

$$10x = 2 \Rightarrow x = \frac{1}{5}$$

$$12x = 9 \Rightarrow x = \frac{3}{4}$$

Here are visual solutions to the first three problems involving dominoes.

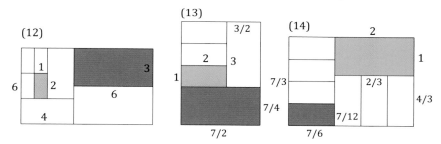

For questions (12) to (14), the ratios are 1 : 3, 4 : 7 and 12 : 7 respectively.

For the last two questions we have:

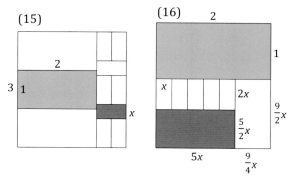

In (15), $\quad x = \dfrac{1}{6} \times 3 = \dfrac{1}{2}$, so the ratio is 2 : 1.

In (16), $\quad 5x + \dfrac{9}{4}x = 2 \;\Rightarrow x = \dfrac{8}{29}$ and $\dfrac{5}{2}x = \dfrac{5}{2} \times \dfrac{8}{29} = \dfrac{20}{29}$.

So the ratio is 29 : 20.

In Problem (17), we might have the figure shown alongside.

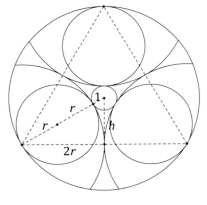

We can use trigonometry to find that

$$h = \frac{2}{\sqrt{3}}r.$$

Then, by Pythagoras' Theorem,

$$(2r + 1)^2 = (2r)^2 + \left(\frac{2}{\sqrt{3}}r\right)^2 = \frac{16}{3}r^2.$$

The ratio of the radius of a green circle to that of the outer circle is $r : 2r + 1$.

Therefore, the ratio of the area of a green circle to that of the outer circle is

$$r^2 : (2r + 1)^2 = r^2 : \frac{16}{3}r^2 = 1 : \frac{16}{3} = 3 : 16.$$

The area of a green circle is $3/16$ of the area of the outer circle and so the three green circles will occupy $9/16$ of the area of the outer circle.

For the second and third cases (Problems 18 and 19), we have:

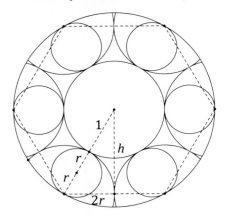

We can use trigonometry to find that $h = 2\sqrt{3}r$.

Then, by Pythagoras' Theorem, $(2r + 1)^2 = (2r)^2 + \left(2\sqrt{3}r\right)^2 = 16r^2.$

The ratio of the radius of a red circle to that of the outer circle is $r : 2r + 1$.
Therefore, the ratio of the area of a red circle to that of the outer circle is

$$r^2 : (2r + 1)^2 = r^2 : 16r^2 = 1 : 16.$$

The area of a red circle is 1/16 of the area of the outer circle and so the six red circles will occupy 3/8 of the area of the outer circle.

Also, the radius of the central circle is half that of the outer circle and hence its area is a quarter that of the outer circle. So the fraction of the outer circle taken up by the seven smaller circles is

$$\frac{3}{8} + \frac{1}{4} = \frac{5}{8}.$$

But we need to rewind a little for a salutary lesson. Of all the mathematical skills the ability to generalise is probably the most telling in terms of the learner's further development. And yet, the urge to generalise without due care and attention is something to be avoided. So, for the circles problems in which we have just the rings of smaller circles on the periphery (i.e. Problems 17 and 18, but not 19), do the results we have to this point really admit of generalisation? Let's try tabulating what we have so far:

Number of small circles or order of symmetry	3	4	5	6	7	8
Fraction	$\dfrac{9}{16}$	$\dfrac{1}{2} = \dfrac{8}{16}$	?	$\dfrac{3}{8} = \dfrac{6}{16}$	?	?

It looks as if the fractions are descending multiples of 1/16, suggesting that when there are five small circles the fraction is 7/16. Yet, a little thought about what happens when the number of small circles is large should deflect us from such thoughts. For the record, for five small squares, 43.186% of the outer circle is occupied, while 7/16 equates to 43.75% – close, but not exact. And for eight small squares, just over 29% of the outer circle is occupied, while 4/16 is 25% – not close at all! The impulse to infer generality here is fatally flawed – a salutary lesson for those who would pursue generalisation slavishly.

3.7 Partial solution to the extension problem

For Problem 20 there are 13 possibilities shown on the next page. Notice how the patterns have been generated and laid out in families (columns).

Possible further extension

How many patterns are there for other numbers of dominoes? What sequence of numbers is produced for 1, 2, 3, 4, ... dominoes? How could binary digits be applied to the patterns and would this help generate the answers?

I hope that this chapter has given you both the enthusiasm to design your own problems for your students and provided some guidance on how to go about it. If so, then occasionally, set the textbook aside and go it alone!

4   *Exploring and Investigating*

4.1 Introduction

In this chapter we consider five scenarios in which learners can explore and investigate mathematics. They are strongly visual in nature, requiring the manipulation of objects or shapes either physically or in the mind's eye. In general, they are more open-ended than the problems in the previous chapter and some youngsters might catch the bug and play around with them for hours.

Packing tetrominoes	A wide-ranging exploration in which shapes are manipulated and possibilities counted. An understanding of symmetry is developed if not previously in place. Suitable for primary pupils as well as secondary.
The power of chess pieces	As it stands this is a closed problem, visual and numerical in nature, but it could be extended by generalising the size of the chess board and, though not undertaken here, this can lead to formula generation and proof by induction. Suitable for upper primary and secondary, though a knowledge of how chess pieces move may be required before starting.
Hextiles	Set in the context of quilting, a short exploration in which increasingly complex patterns are built, followed by a tessellation activity. Perhaps start very 'hands-on' using hexagonal 'board game tiles'. Suitable for upper primary and upwards.
Matchsticks	Exploring simple shapes with a fixed perimeter but different areas. Then change the perimeter and explore further. Generating results from earlier results. Suitable for upper primary but with elements that are exclusively secondary.
Equable polygons	A more complex investigation suitable for secondary pupils only, taking care that they do not conflate the concepts of perimeter and area. Includes some elementary number theory.

The first three of these investigations are new, the fourth appeared as 'The twelve matchstick diversion', in *SMC Journal* 45 (2015), pp. 27-36, and the last as 'Equal perimeter and area; what a strange notion!' in *SMC Journal* 47 (2017), pp. 52-57.

4.2 Packing Tetrominoes

A 'tetromino' is a shape made from four squares stuck together, edge to edge. There are five of them, dubbed *straight, T, square, L* and *Z*.

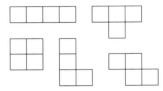

All of the tetrominoes tessellate, that is, they can be used to tile the plane. But what if we introduce a constraint, packing them into a given shape such as a square, and what if we use as many (or as few) of a particular tetromino as necessary? It would give us a framework for three investigations and a game of strategy:

1. Optimal packing: finding the maximum numbers of tetrominoes that can be positioned inside squares of different sizes.
2. Minimum packing: finding the minimum numbers of tetrominoes that can be positioned inside squares of different sizes.
3. Finding all distinct solutions to the optimal packing investigation for a specific square.
4. Game: in turn, two players place tetrominoes until one of them (the loser) cannot move.

1. Optimal packing

Consider packing a 3 × 3 square just with L-tetrominoes. Since the square has only nine component unit squares, the maximum number of L-tetrominoes is two. One way this might be represented is by connecting the centres of the unit squares and finishing by shading any unused squares.

Solutions arising from a rotation or a reflection of this pattern are deemed equivalent.

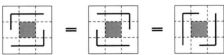

In other words, there is only one solution here.

The 4 × 4 square has 16 unit squares and since 16 is a multiple of 4, it might be possible to find a perfect packing. In fact, it is possible; here are the three solutions:

Investigation Explore packing each of the tetrominoes in turn in squares of various sizes. What is the maximum number of tetrominoes in each square? Is it possible to predict when there will be a perfect packing? What is the maximum number of tetrominoes in each square? Generalise, conjecture and prove, wherever possible.

Some findings

This is an open-ended investigation, so the list of what could be discovered is almost endless. Here are some results.

Straight tetrominoes

When maximising the number of straights there is a very convenient pattern which cannot be bettered. Here are possible solutions for squares up to side 9.

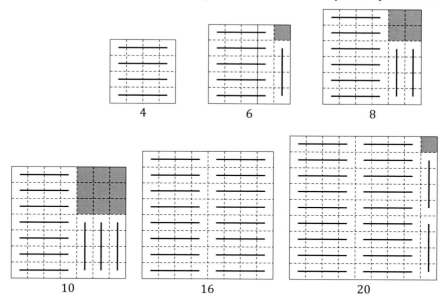

When generalising, we could focus on the unoccupied squares (shaded). There are four cases, depending on whether the side of the square is a multiple of 4 or leaves a remainder of 1, 2, or 3 when divided by 4. Here, $k \geq 1, k \in \mathbb{Z}$.

If $n = 4k$, there are no unoccupied squares;
if $n = 4k + 1$, there is 1 unoccupied square;
if $n = 4k + 2$, there are 4 unoccupied squares;
if $n = 4k + 3$, there are 9 unoccupied squares.

The maximum number of straights, M, is the number of occupied squares divided by 4:

$$M = \begin{cases} \dfrac{1}{4}n^2, & n = 4k \\[2mm] \dfrac{1}{4}(n^2 - 1), & n = 4k + 1 \\[2mm] \dfrac{1}{4}(n^2 - 4), & n = 4k + 2 \\[2mm] \dfrac{1}{4}(n^2 - 9), & n = 4k + 3 \end{cases}$$

If $n = 10$, there are 4 unoccupied squares, leaving 96 occupied by 24 straights.
If $n = 11$, there are 9 unoccupied squares, leaving 112 occupied by 28 straights.
If $n = 12$, all 144 squares are occupied, so 36 straights are required.

We could look at a square of side 23 more closely. Since the diagram is too complex to draw in detail, a schematic or skeleton figure is used.

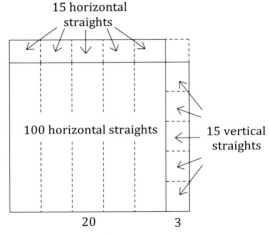

Since $23 = 4 \times 5 + 3$, there will be 5 columns of horizontal straight tetrominoes within a 20 by 20 square, each column holding 20 such straights. The column to the right has width 3 and so will hold 5 sets of 3 vertical straights and the top rectangle is of the same dimensions and will hold 5 sets of 3 horizontal straights. So the total is $100 + 2 \times 15 = 130$.

Is this consistent with the formulas? For a square of side 23, the last formula is the one to use. Substituting $n = 23$, we have:

$$M = \frac{1}{4}(23^2 - 9) = \frac{1}{4} \times 520 = 130.$$

Square tetrominoes

The simplest solutions are shown below for squares of sides 3 to 9:

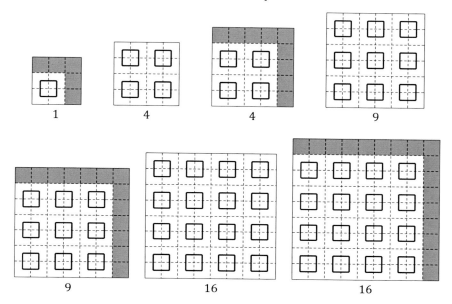

The maximum number of square tetrominoes in squares of different sizes turns out to be much more straightforward than for the straights. For squares of even sides, there is a perfect fit, so

$$M = \left(\frac{1}{2}n\right)^2 = \frac{1}{4}n^2, \qquad n = 2k, k \geq 1$$

But as we move from a particular square of side $2n$ to the next size up, from 4 to 5, from 6 to 7 and so on, all we can do is wrap an L-shaped strip in which no additional square tetrominoes will fit. So for squares of odd sides,

$$M = \left(\frac{1}{2}(n-1)\right)^2 = \frac{1}{4}(n-1)^2, \qquad n = 2k+1, k \geq 1$$

Senior students might be asked to prove these formulas by induction.

L-tetrominoes

For the L-tetrominoes, the parity of the order of the outer square is critical. If the number of squares on one side of the square is odd, we have one set of results and if it is even we have another. Let's look at the odds, and in particular at squares of order 5, 7 and 9. They contain 25, 49 and 81 unit squares respectively, each being one more than a multiple of 4.

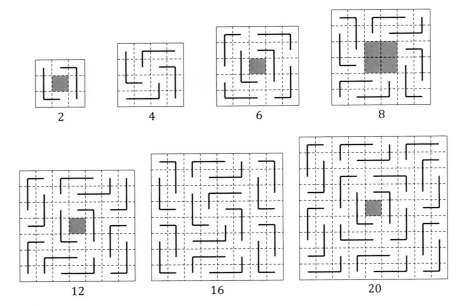

It seems perfectly reasonable to explore cases which are symmetrical about a central unused cell. This is what results (remembering that reflections are equivalent):

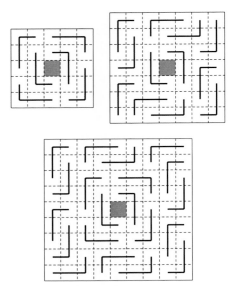

It appears that the maximum number of L-tetrominoes in a square of odd side is simply

$$M = \frac{1}{4}(n^2 - 1), \quad n = 2k + 1, n \geq 1$$

Note that the solution for the square of side 5 is that of the square of side 3 with 4 L-tetrominoes wrapped around in a corridor of unit width. The solution for the square of side 7 is that of the square of side 3 with 10 L-tetrominoes wrapped around in a corridor of width 2. The solution for the square of side 9 is that of the square of side 5 with 14 L-tetrominoes wrapped around in a corridor of width 2. Indeed, such corridors can always be constructed. The square of side 11 has the design for the square of side 7 with an additional corridor of width 2. This in itself provides a very credible demonstration of the result.

What happens when we pack L-tetrominoes into squares of even side, $2n$? Well we know that four L-tetrominoes fit inside a 4×4 square perfectly. The 6×6 square has 36 cells suggesting that 9 L-shaped tiles might fit tightly... and yet they don't. The most that can be fitted is 8 and here are three symmetrical ways in which this can be done:

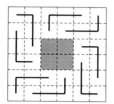 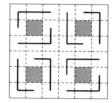 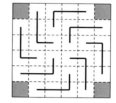

The first has similarities to the solution suggested above for the 7×7 square; the second is simply four copies of the 3×3 design, in a sense an even number of odds; the third appears to be based on the suggested 4×4 solution. Also note that the symmetry is achieved by having the four unused squares on the diagonals.

Packing L-tetrominoes in an 8×8 square will be perfect, i.e. with no empty cells. One way (not the only way) of achieveing this is by using four copies of the perfect 4×4 design.

Overall, perhaps the wrap-around or corridor approach is again the best. Solutions for squares of side 4, 6, 8 and 10 are shown on the next page. They may be classified as even-even or odd-even, i.e. $n = 4k$ or $n = 4n + 2$ $(k \geq 1)$ and the maximum number of L-tetrominoes is:

$$M = \begin{cases} \dfrac{1}{4}n^2, & n = 4k \\ \dfrac{1}{4}(n-1)^2, & n = 4k + 2 \end{cases}$$

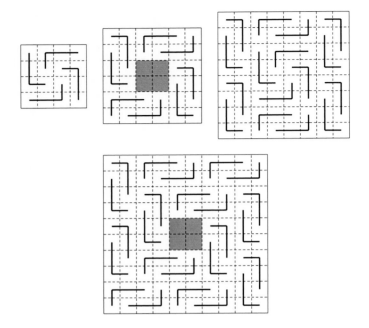

T-tetrominoes

The maximum number of T-tetrominoes in squares of increasing size does not appear to generalise easily (if at all). For those with an unquestioning faith in the prevalence of pattern, this provides a salutory counterexample.

The 4×4 case provides a neat, perfect packing which can be used as a template for all squares of side $4n$.

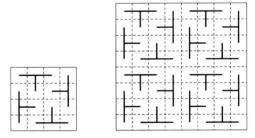

Here are three solutions for the 5×5 square. Depending on your way of thinking, the first has some merit, the second and third perhaps less so.

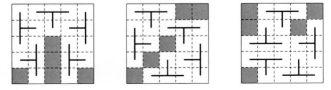

At the very least, we can say that the maximum number of T-tetrominoes that can be packed in a 5 × 5 square is just five. The two examples below are of the maximum eight T-shapes in a 6 × 6 square, the first with bilateral symmetry, the second with point symmetry (rotational symmetry of order 2).

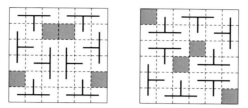

Now, let's jump to the 9 × 9 square for this pleasing design which features 12 T-tiles and some translational symmetry:

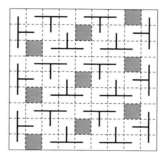

To summarise, here's a set of possibilities for squares of sides 3 to 9.

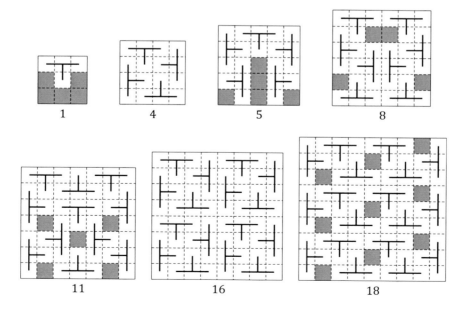

Z-tetrominoes

Examples of optimal solutions are shown below for the Z-tetrominoes.

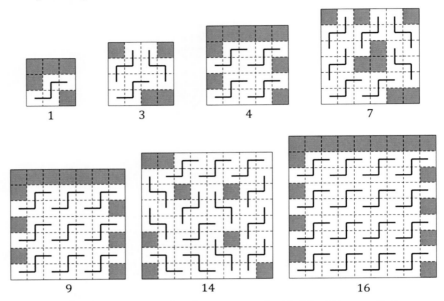

A noteworthy observation is that for squares of odd side, M is a perfect square. To be precise, if $n = 2k + 1$, then $M = k^2$. My suspicion is that there is no pattern in the maximum number of Z-tetrominoes that can be placed inside a square of even side ... but perhaps you know better!

2. Minimum packing

Now for the complementary task of finding the fewest tiles that can be placed inside squares of different sizes. Some examples of minima are shown on the next three pages. They are not unique. There appear to be no obvious patterns for any of the five different tetrominoes except the squares, so let's focus on them alone.

For squares of side 2 and upwards, the minimum number of square tetrominoes, m, that can be placed is

$$1, 1, 1, 4, 4, 4, 9, 9, 9, 16, 16, 16, ...$$

Given a particular member of a triple the other two can be found by the judicious creation of external or internal 'corridors'. We can formalise the situation in this way:

$$m = k^2, \quad \text{for } n = 3k - 1, 3k, 3k + 1$$

For example, take the case of a square of side 11, i.e. $n = 11$. Now $11 = 3k - 1$ where $k = 4$. So the minimum number of square tetrominoes in a square of side 11 is $4^2 = 16$.

Straight tetrominoes

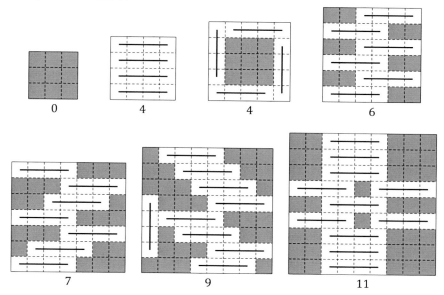

Square tetrominoes

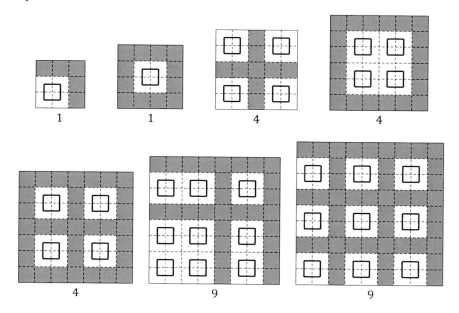

L-tetrominoes

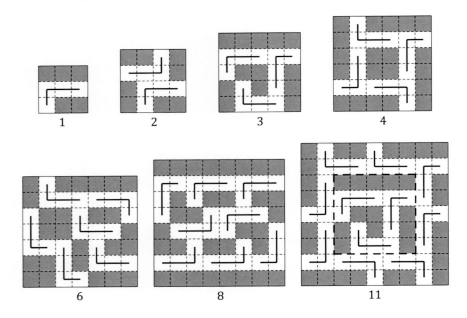

T-tetrominoes

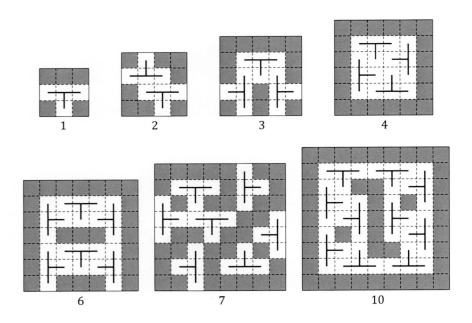

Z-tetrominoes

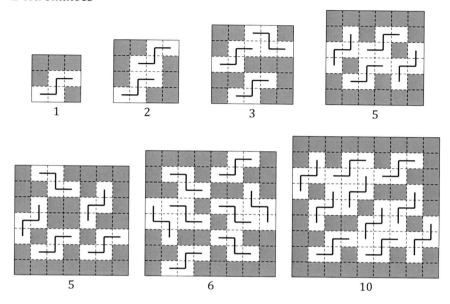

| 1 | 2 | 3 | 5 |

| 5 | 6 | 10 |

3.   All distinct solutions

The key considerations here are the choice of tetromino and the choice of square size. As to the second, any size below the 5 × 5 provides little challenge and anything above throws up too many possibilities. But even if we settle on the 5 × 5, not all five tetrominoes afford a suitable challenge. In particular, if the straight tetromino is chosen the problem is trivial. Both the square and L-tetrominoes are ideal, the T-tetromino is more demanding and the Z-tetromino is unsuitable because of the very large number of solutions. We will focus on the square, T- and L-tetrominoes. By beginning with the T's, we can show how a full set can be developed in systematic fashion.

T-tetrominoes

Let's first fix four T's as in the left-hand figure below. This also fixes an unused square in the bottom left, shaded dark grey. The remaining eight squares (pale grey) can be used to insert just one further T and this can be done in six ways.

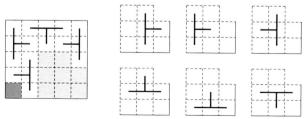

In other words, there are six solutions which have those particular four T-tetrominoes fixed from the outset. In the figure below, each has been given a bracketed label so that reference can be made to them for checking purposes.

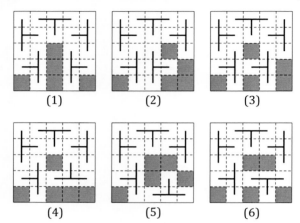

Now, keeping three of the T-terominoes in place, the fourth is repositioned and this leaves just five unoccupied squares and a single solution. But we've already got it. It's solution (2), reflected!

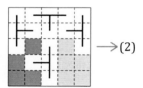

Another repositioning of the fourth T this leaves nine unoccupied squares. A fifth 'upside-down' T can be inserted in one of two positions but they are mirror images of each other. Either of them provides a valid seventh solution. A good way to check (though not a fail-safe way) is to examine the patterns in the unusued squares.

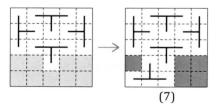

The fourth T can be postioned in just one more place and this gives a further two new solutions.

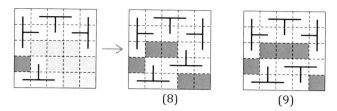

To continue, we fix fewer squares and reach a further thirteen solutions.

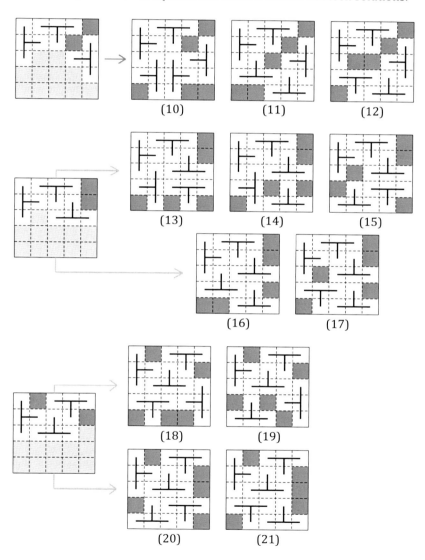

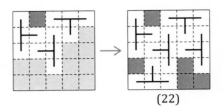

(22)

L-tetrominoes

Six L-tetrominoes can be fitted in a number of ways, leaving a single blank square. A little experimentation and a consideration of symmetry suggests that the blank must be either in the centre or in a corner. There are two groups of the former and two groups of the latter, shown here on separate rows.

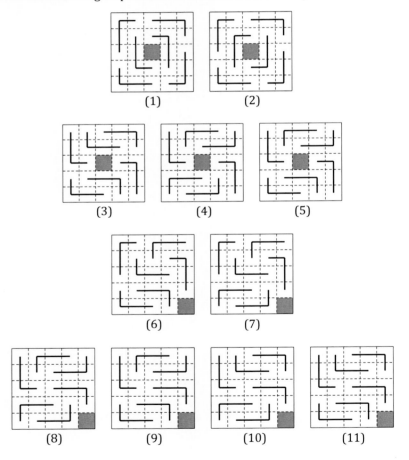

Square tetrominoes

Just the solutions this time! Did you find them all?

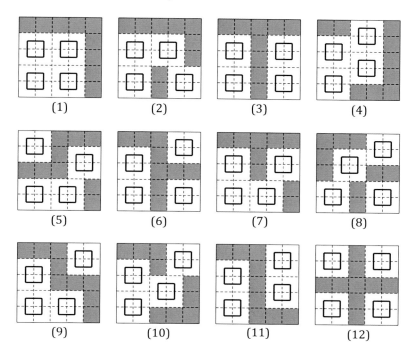

'Chessboard Tetro'

Here's a strategy game for two players who take turns at placing square tetrominoes on the grid until one of them cannot move. The size of the grid is important because if it's too small then the game is over after very few moves and if it's too big it will last too long. Not only is the 8 × 8 grid ideal but in practice a chessboard can be used. So let's refer to the game as 'Chessboard Tetro' to differentiate it from any other tetro-game that's out there! In the examples that follow, the moves of the first player are shown in black, those of the second player in grey, and the squares that are put out of commission by the moves are shaded light grey. Here are the first seven moves of a possible game:

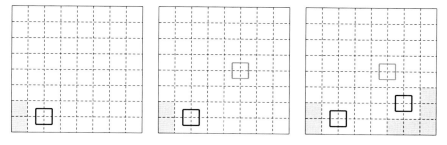

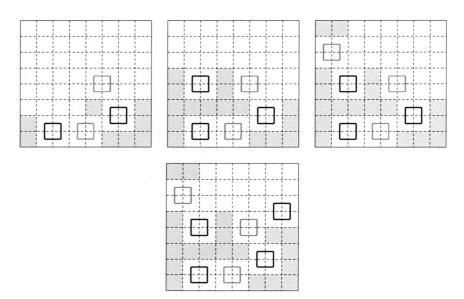

If the game does develop this way then the next move by the second player becomes crucial strategically. Of the seven possible positions for the square tetromino (filled), the first player can respond with a winning move (also filled).

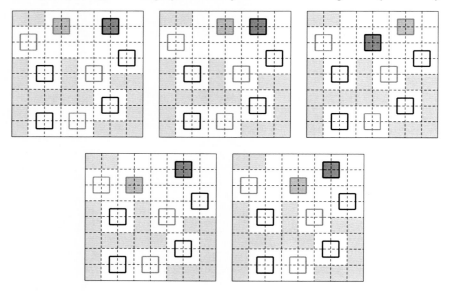

But there are two possible moves that guarantee a win for the second player. Can you see why?

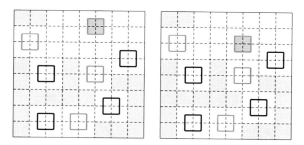

The game could be played on a chessboard using any of the other tetrominoes.

Trying out the activities

Some of the activities were tried out with two of my grandsons, both strong mathematically for their ages, Jonah (aged 6) and Ewan (aged 8).

Working separately, Jonah experimented until he came up with a correct solution to the minimum number of square tetrominoes on a chessboard (below left), then Ewan produced a solution he clearly liked (right), excitingly commenting that it had "symmetry four ways".

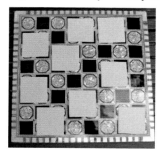 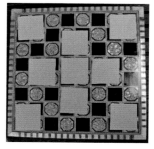

When I brought the boys together and explained the rules and objectives of 'Chessboard Tetro', they had a go at the game. One of them was given a set of blank cards, the other a set with a white square stuck on the back of each.

Unfortunately, the white squares don't show up particularly well in the photograph below, so I have superimposed black crosses.

'Cross' moved first and then they took turns until both had made four moves. The fifth move by cross stopped any further squares being placed, so cross won. You may wish to explore whether the player going first can always force a win. And you might try the game using a 9 × 9 board (though you may have to draw it yourself), where the number of cards placed before the game is won is greater, especially if used in a secondary classroom.

Finally Jonah and Ewan worked together on T-tetrominoes. They enjoyed placing 16 T's systematically and incorporating symmetry without prompting.

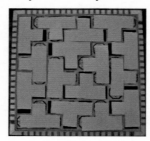 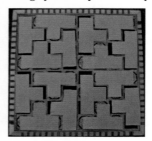

But they found the task of placing as few as possible T's more demanding, successively finding solutions with 10, 9 and 8 T's but not the minimum 7.

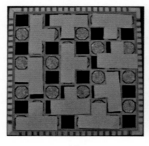 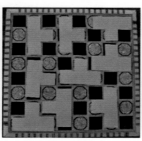 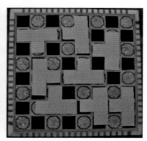

         10   9   8

4.3 The Power of Chess Pieces

In chess the pieces move in different ways. Some are quite restricted in what they can do and how fast they can move while others can move quickly and with dramatic effect. Pawns are weak, Bishops are stronger, Queens are positively dangerous. One way in which the relative powers of the pieces are recognised is through a points system:

♟	Pawn	1
♝	Bishop	3
♞	Knight	3
♜	Rook	5
♛	Queen	9

The King can take other pieces but his role is simply to survive and so he is not included in the points system.

Lewis Chessmen: National Museums Scotland, CC BY-SA 4.0,
https://commons.wikimedia.org/w/index.php?curid=83115741

Does this points system truly reflect the relative power of the pieces? Here's a mathematical investigation for 12-15 year olds that aims to find out.

Chess Power

Assumption: One way to judge the power of a chess piece is to calculate the number of squares it threatens. For each piece, the number of squares that can be reached from a particular position is checked and this is repeated for all possible positions and the total calculated. Then a comparison is made with the totals for the other pieces.

Here's a reminder of how the pieces move.

- Pawns move upwards from their starting positions on the second rank and can take opposing pieces that are one square ahead on the diagonal.

- Bishops move on the diagonal, threatening any piece between them and the edge of the board.

- Knights move in a complex pattern, 2 squares one way and one square at right angles. They are the only pieces that can jump over pieces 'in the way', though this will be ignored here.

- Rooks move up and down and sideways to the edge of the board.

- Queens move up, down and sideways (as if a Rook) and diagonally (as if a Bishop) to the edge of the board.

- Kings move as the Queen but only one square.

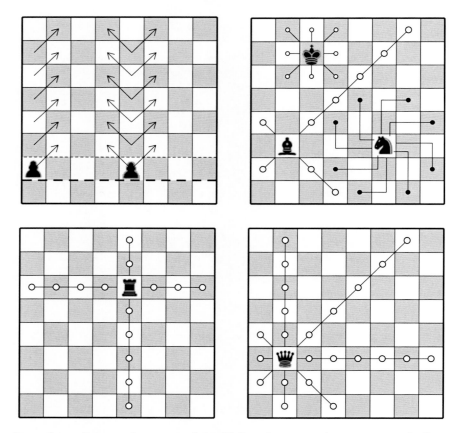

From these diagrams it appears that a Bishop threatens nine squares and a King threatens eight but this is not always so because the number of squares threatened depends on their current positions. In the diagram below the Bishop is threatening seven squares and the King just five.

114

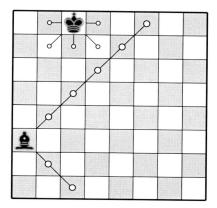

Perhaps with prompting on an individual or class level, this is what might be discovered.

For the Pawns we have a restricted board. Except in highly unlikely circumstances Pawns do not visit the first rank and if they reach the eighth rank there are complications which make the calculations impossible. The first and last rank are therefore ignored to avoid complications.

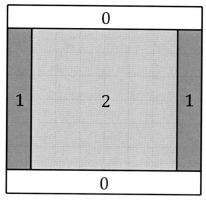

If a Pawn is on an edge square between the second and seventh ranks it can reach just one square, if in the central block it can reach two squares. So the power of the Pawn is

$$12 \times 1 + 36 \times 2 = 72.$$

Bishops threaten more and more squares the nearer they are to the middle of the board. If they are on an edge square they threaten seven, if one square in they threaten nine and so on.

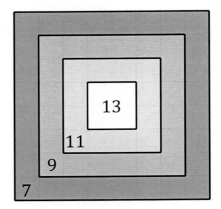

The number of squares in these 'rings' is 28, 20, 12 and 4 respectively, and so the power of the Bishop is

$$28 \times 7 + 20 \times 9 + 12 \times 11 + 4 \times 13 = 560.$$

The movement of the Knight is weird and wonderful and this requires more detailed analysis. Here is that analysis in visual form.

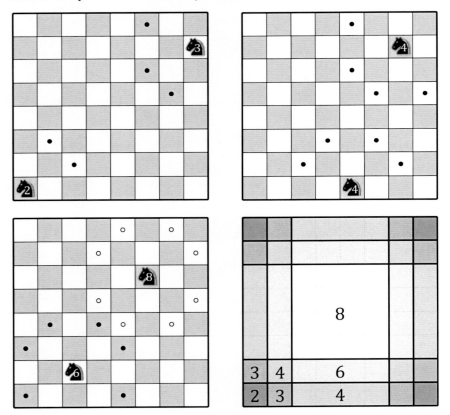

If the Knight is on a corner square only two squares are threatened and if next to a corner on the edge, three are threatened. There are two positions in which four squares are threatened – an edge square two or more away from the corners and a position on the diagonal one square in from the corner. Six squares can be reached from four positions on the second rank and their equivalents after rotation, and from any of the squares in the large block in the middle eight can be reached. The power of the Knight is therefore:

$$4 \times 2 + 8 \times 3 + (16 + 4) \times 4 + 16 \times 6 + 16 \times 8 = 336.$$

From any square on the board, the Rook can reach seven squares on its rank (row) and seven squares on its file (column). So immediately, its power is just $64 \times 14 = 896$.

Here's a visual summary for the power of the Queen:

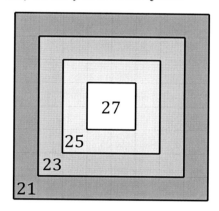

The required sum can be reached by one of two routes.

a) From the diagram, $28 \times 21 + 20 \times 23 + 12 \times 25 + 8 \times 27 = 1456$,
b) Summing the powers for the Bishop and Rook: $560 + 896 = 1456$.

Tabulating our results we have:

Piece		Power	Standard score
	Pawn	72	1
	Bishop	560	3
	Knight	336	3
	Rook	896	5
	Queen	1456	9

Two things immediately appear at odds with the standard scoring system. Firstly, the power of the Pawn (only about 1/20 of the power of the Queen) is unusually low. Secondly, there is a mismatch between the power of the Bishop and the power of the Knight. Both issues might be explained by acknowledging that our assumptions were incomplete, at best, or fatally flawed. Remember that we did not allow the pawn to reach the eighth rank (where it could be exchanged for a Queen, or indeed any other piece); there must be some inherent loss of power as a result. Also, Pawns are never on the first rank. So we have only considered Pawns on 48 squares, while all other pieces have been considered over the whole board. So let's compensate by increasing the calculated power of the Pawn by 64/48 or 4/3. The revised power would be 96 (which is still unexpectedly low). As to the Bishop and the Knight, remember that the Knight can jump over other pieces while the Bishop will typically be blocked by them but since there was no way to incorporate that in our model, the power of the Knight has suffered accordingly.

These issues are evident if we scale the powers so that that of the Pawn is reduced from 96 to 1.

Piece		Power scaled to Pawn	Standard score
♟	Pawn	1	1
♝	Bishop	5.8	3
♞	Knight	3.5	3
♜	Rook	9.3	5
♛	Queen	15.2	9

Inevitably, scaling to the flawed Pawn power is no success, so instead let's rescale so that Rook is assigned the power 5 as in the standard scoring scheme. Then we have a reasonable approximation to that standard scheme.

Piece		Power scaled to Rook	Rounded scaled power	Standard score
♟	Pawn	0.54	1	1
♝	Bishop	3.125	3	3
♞	Knight	1.875	2	3
♜	Rook	5	5	5
♛	Queen	8.125	8	9

Variations on the standard scoring scheme have been suggested over the years, sometimes by the giants of the game, including the longest ever reigning World Champion, Emanuel Lasker (1868–1941), who was also a fine mathematician. More details are at https://en.wikipedia.org/wiki/Chess_piece_relative_value. Lasker suggested a score of 8.5 for the Queen!

4.4 Hextiles for textiles

Quilting is a popular hobby and can be a source of pleasure and achievement. Often the component shapes are regular hexagons. They may be combined to make recognisable patterns or arranged into more random designs. Here's one that suggest flower heads.

'Hexagon paper pieced quilt under production', Wikimedia,
Creative Commons Attribution-Share Alike 2.0 Generic License

Regular hexagons can be stuck together to make different shapes, not just flower heads. These shapes don't seem to have a standard name, so let's call them 'hextiles'. After all, they are made of **hex**agons and can be used to **tile** the plane (i.e. they tessellate), and furthermore they can be used with **t**extiles. The pieces should join along an edge not just at the corners (vertices). There is only one way two regular hexagons can be fitted together:

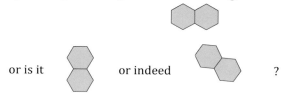

or is it   or indeed   ?

Well, it doesn't matter because we consider them to be the same. There is only one 2-hextile. In fact, not only can we turn them around, but we can flip them over as well if we wish and this might be important when we come to 3-hextiles and 4-hextiles.

Tasks

1. Find all the hextiles that can be built from three hexagons and from four hexagons (i.e. all the 3-hextiles and 4-hextiles).
2. Show how each of the 4-hextiles tessellate.

Solutions

1. The solutions can be built up by accretion, adding an extra hexagon to a design already known, like this:

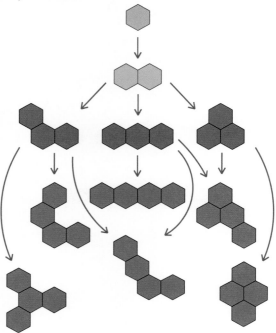

There are three 3-hextiles, coloured blue. Each of them can be created from the 2-hextile by attaching a hexagon in a different way. And there are six 4-hextiles. In four cases they can be made by adding a hexagon to a particular 3-hextile, and in the other two cases they can be made from either of two 3-hextiles.

If this task catches the imagination of the learners, extending to 5-hextiles is obviously a possibility. However, pushing further still is complex and fraught with potential problems, including shapes with holes in them. Best left alone!

2. The tessellations shown below may not be unique.

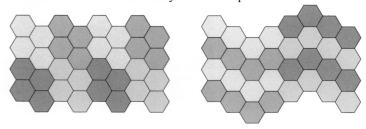

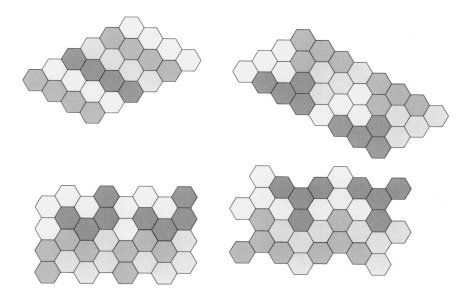

4.5 Matchsticks

Preamble

How often do we see the calculation of the perimeter of a shape confused with the calculation of its area? Are the concepts of perimeter and area poorly understood, wholly different though they are? Are perimeter and area formulas learnt in rote fashion and retrieved carelessly? Is it plain panic on the part of examinees under pressure that leads to any formula being used? Rather perversely, in what follows, we offer the obvious advice of keeping the two concepts separate and then explore situations in which they are deliberately brought together. Perhaps the two explorations are suitable only for those who have already understood the concepts well or as a means of strengthening understanding.

The case for keeping perimeter and area separate is obvious and yet textbook writers predominantly shove them together, most notoriously with regard to the circle. It is as if the shape rather than the concepts dominate the agenda. But perimeter means to measure around, to measure a length, to walk around the boundary. It has dimension 1, its formula must have a 1-D variable and the units in which it is stated have unit dimension too. For a circle we have $C = \pi d$, the units being mm, cm, m, km, etc. By contrast, area is what's inside a boundary line or circumference. It has dimension 2, its formula must have a 2-D variable, or two 1-D variables and be stated in 2-D units. For a circle we have $A = \pi r^2$, with units mm², cm², m², km². Unfortunately, at least in this regard, the use of *hectares* or indeed *acres* is not helpful. The advice then is to teach all perimeter first, including the circumference of a circle, and all area later, including the area

121

of a circle. And if at all unsure, checks can be made on the exponents of the variables and the units.

The twelve matchstick diversion

Here is a mathematical 'diversion' or open investigation inspired by Martin Gardner; it is an exploration of the areas of figures with fixed perimeter. Take a dozen matches and join them end to end to produce the boundary of a shape with an integral number of units of area. Investigate the possible areas. The task can be tackled using a large supply of dead matches (or equivalent) in hands-on fashion, using pencil and squared paper, or using a computer, laptop or tablet.

It would be a good idea to give a couple of examples, perhaps these with areas 5 and 6:

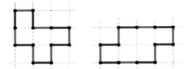

Working in twos or threes, about twenty minutes should suffice to generate a lot of shapes and their areas. Among the issues that will be raised is whether a shape that is a reflection or rotation of one already produced can be counted as different, as in these pairs:

Be prepared for questions such as, 'How many different shapes are possible?' or 'What's the greatest possible area possible?' Both are easily countered with, 'That's for you to find out.' Then there's, 'Can I put a match on the diagonal?' which should engender some class discussion of varying sophistication depending on whether Pythagoras' Theorem has yet been encountered.

The class may produce a comprehensive list like the one on the next page. In amongst these patterns there are many which feature in another activity promoted by Gardner, namely, Solomon Golomb's polyominoes. For example, the last set of shapes, those with area 5, form an incomplete set of pentominoes, shapes which can be made by sticking together five squares so that the joins are fully edge-to-edge.

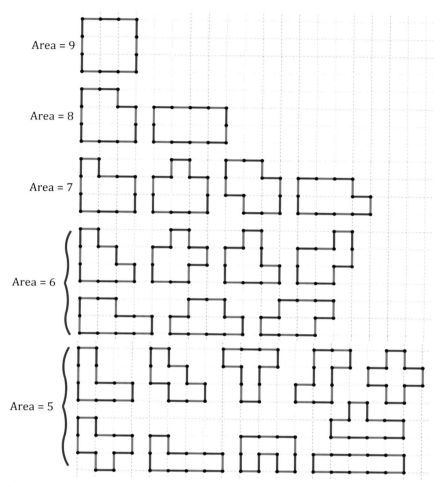

The only missing one is the unique pentomino with perimeter 10:

Later we will use polyominoes as 'blanks' to forge different shapes on a near industrial scale. Meanwhile, we simply ask whether the twelve matches can be arranged to form a triangle with an integral area. One consequence is that not all the matches can lie along the grid lines; specifically, in a right-angled triangle, which is where the pupils should look or be directed to look, the hypotenuse must leave the grid. Sure enough, the (3, 4, 5) triangle works a treat. It has area $\frac{1}{2} \times 4 \times 3 = 6$.

And we can explore variations on a theme, cutting into the basic design step by step.

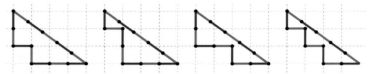

These designs have areas 5, 4, 4 and 3 respectively.

There are two even more ingenious solutions, given at the wonderful 'cut-the-knot' website, developed by Alexander Bogomolny. Both make use of the device of reflecting part of the perimeter (4 matches and 5 matches) so that the basic triangle is folded onto itself.

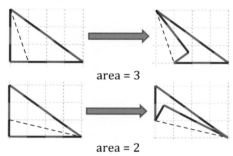

To summarise, we have found designs with perimeter 12 and areas of all integral values from 9 right down to 2.

Cross-overs

It is also possible to produce cross-overs or crossed polygons, such as those shown alongside. Here, the very first encloses area 5, the next seven enclose area 4 and the last two enclose area 3.

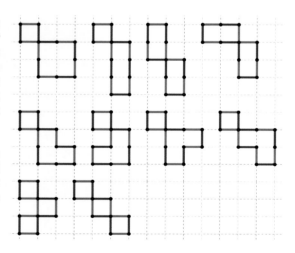

Do we have them all or have some been missed? And should we allow them at all? What does your class think?

Moving off the grid

If we begin with a shape that tessellates, such as a square, rectangle or rhombus, we can add something to a side whilst removing a congruent shape from the opposite side, as in these examples:

The second figure is produced from the initial square by adding a semicircle on top whilst cutting a semicircle from the bottom. The third figure is just the second with added and subtracted triangles. And the tiling looks like this:

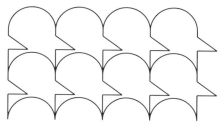

As we extend the Twelve Matchstick Diversion into this territory, our tack is to add and subtract equilateral triangles to some 'blank'. As we change from say three matches in a row to a section of the perimeter incorporating one equilateral triangle, we need an extra match:

So the adding and removing of one triangle requires two additional matches, or equivalently, we need to reduce the area of the blank by two units to accommodate the two kinks in the boundary.

Take a design with area 8 and perimeter 12:

If we were to add and remove triangles, we would get, say:

This figure has area 8, but perimeter 14 which is no good. Instead, we need to start with a blank rectangle with area 6 and perimeter 10

and produce a figure with area 6 and perimeter 12 (as required), like this, maybe:

So how many blanks of perimeter 10 are there? Every such form that we find will give a new set of patterns. Time to take another break and let the class take the strain.

Blanks of perimeter 10

Now we are back in polyomino territory. Hopefully, the class will come up with the hexomino and the following four tetrominoes:

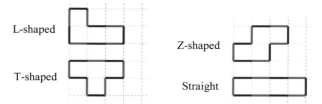

Generating the possible patterns is a huge task and one best tackled by the whole class, perhaps working in small groups and adding their patterns to a giant wall poster. There are two ways to proceed, one *ad hoc* and the other, algorithmically. In the first, patterns are generated in any order by any or no process and checked individually against the current bank of patterns in case they are rotations or reflections of any of them. In the second, all possible patterns are produced and the 'copies' wiped out in one fell swoop at the end. This is perhaps how we would operate if we were to use a computer program to produce the patterns. For the sake of completeness, at least in this part of the chapter, we show all the patterns and provide comments on the symmetries.

Using the hexomino, we can produce the first subset in the following way. Produce the bulge at the top left. Then the cut is made where the next line segment would have been to its right. The next pattern leaves the bulge unchanged but moves the cut around one position clockwise and so on for the remaining patterns in the subset, as shown in the strip at the bottom of the page.

Then, changing the position of the bulge systematically produces more subsets.

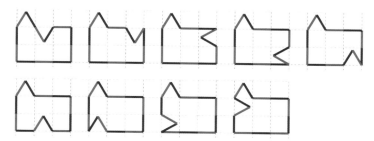

The full set consists of 36 different patterns once the replicates arising through reflection and rotation are discarded.

The same process can be carried out on the four tetrominoes and the number of patterns this produces is 90, 46, 45 and 45 respectively. The grand total is therefore 262. (There is insufficient space to show all of them here.)

Further exploration

(1) *Double additions and subtractions*

Pupils can explore patterns such as these:

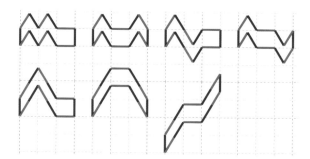

or these patterns, and their friends:

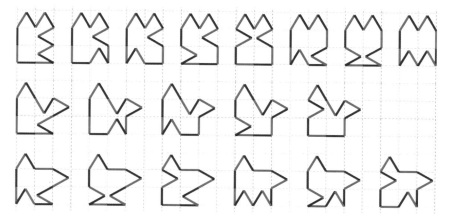

(2) *Breaking the rules*

We can make use of this diversion to practise work on Pythagoras' Theorem and trigonometry, simply by abandoning the original requirement that the areas have integral values only. Here's a nice group of five designs:

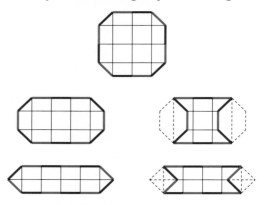

... and here, some skeleton workings:

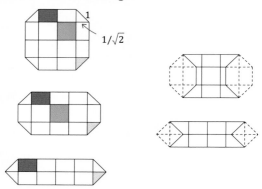

The respective areas are: $5 + 4\sqrt{2}, 4 + 4\sqrt{2}, 1 + 4\sqrt{2}, 2 + 2\sqrt{2}, -1 + 4\sqrt{2}$.

Here are two more (with areas $6\sqrt{3}$ and $3\sqrt{3}$):

Finally, the greatest area enclosed by twelve matchsticks of unit length is found if they are arranged in the shape of a regular dodecagon:

To find the area of the dodecagon, it is helpful to know the distance from the shape's centre to a vertex (or its square):

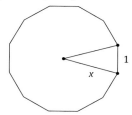

By the Cosine Rule:

$$2x^2 - 2x^2 \cos 30° = 1$$
$$x^2(2 - \sqrt{3}) = 1$$
$$x^2 = \frac{1}{2 - \sqrt{3}} = 2 + \sqrt{3}.$$

Area of dodecagon is:

$$12 \times \frac{1}{2}(2 + \sqrt{3}) \sin 30° = 3(2 + \sqrt{3}).$$

Writing this expression in the form:

$$6 + 12\left(\frac{\sqrt{3}}{4}\right)$$

sits nicely with a visual, dissection solution:

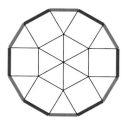

Reference

Gardner, M. 'The twelve matches', in *Mathematical Puzzles and Diversions*, Pelican (1971), p 101.

Afterword

Having given a talk on the matchsticks diversion at the Mathematical Association Annual Conference at Keele University one year, Jim Simons emailed me with the following observation:

> You can make an area of 1 square unit with 12 matches, using a parallelogram.

> One match goes from $(0,0)$ to $(1,0)$, and a parallel one goes from $(\sqrt{24}, 1)$ to $(1 + \sqrt{24}, 1)$, with 5 other matches making each of the other two sides.

> By varying the length of the base, and keeping the height 1, you can make areas of 1, 2, 3, 4 and 5. By making the height 2 you can make 2, 4, 6 and 8, and by making the height 3, you can make 3, 6 and 9.

4.6 Equable polygons

A square of side 4 m has perimeter 16 m and area 16 m². A rectangle of base 6 cm and height 3 cm has perimeter 18 cm and area 18 cm². In each case, the shape's perimeter and area are numerically equal. (Of course, a perimeter cannot equal an area because the former is a measurement in 1 dimension and the latter is a measurement in 2 dimensions. But we can say that a perimeter and an area are **numerically equal** in the sense that if we leave aside the units we get the same number.) Polygons which have integer side lengths in addition to this property are termed 'equable' and the two cases we have looked at are the only two equable rectangles.

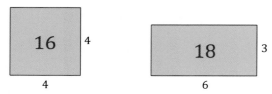

To prove this is so, we take a rectangle of base x and height y. The condition that the perimeter P and area A are equal is:

$$xy = 2(x + y)$$
$$y(x - 2) = 2x$$
$$y = \frac{2x}{x - 2}.$$

Now if both x and y are positive integers, $x \geq y$, we can trawl for valid solutions by substituting possible dimensions of the base ($x = 4,5,6 \dots$) into the formula for y to find the associated heights.

$x = 4, y = 4$ $P = A = 16$
$x = 5, y = 10/3$
$x = 6, y = 3$ $P = A = 18$
$x = 7, y = 14/5$
$x = 8, y = 8/3$
$x = 9, y = 18/7$
$x = 10, y = 5/2$
$x = 11, y = 22/9$ and so on.

All but two of the integer values of x yield non-integer values of y and these relate to the two cases of **equable rectangles** we have already noted, the square of side 4 and the rectangle of base 6 and height 3.

The question of just how many **equable triangles** there are was first posed in 1828, but it took until 1904 for a solution to be found. In that year William Allen Whitworth (1840–1905) found all five cases and Daniel Biddle (1840–1924) noted that while two of them are right-angled triangles and as such rather easily spotted, the other three arise from removing a right-angled triangle from another right-angled triangle. In the figure below, the common perimeter/area is shown in blue. A derivation of the five is given in Palfreyman(2015).

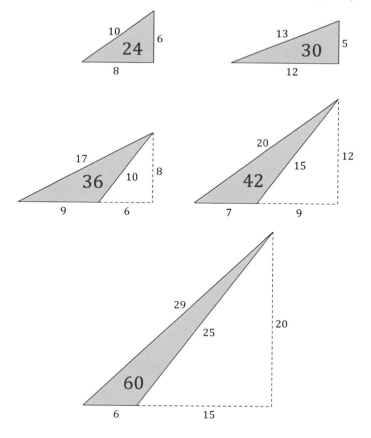

Equable triangles have the property that their incircles are the same size. Here is a composite diagram, showing the first right-angled equable triangles superimposed and likewise the three obtuse-angled triangles.

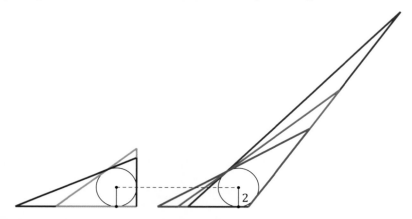

The length of the inradius can be found from Heron, who showed that for any triangle $A = rs$, where the three variables are its area, inradius and semi-perimeter, respectively. In the special circumstance that its perimeter and area are equal, then $2A = 2rs = rA$. Hence $r = 2$. Equable triangles have inradius 2.

It is possible to find triangles with not only the same perimeter as each other, but also the same area as each other. Such a pair is the (20,21,29) right-angled triangle and the (17,25,28) triangle made up of two right-angled triangles stuck together. In each case the perimeter is 70, the area is 210, and the inradius is 6.

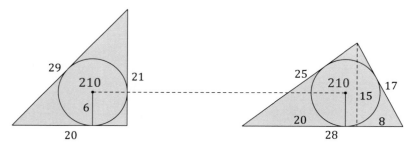

In recent times, there has been a search for other equable polygons, especially by Stan Dolan. Here is his method for finding equable trapezia by splitting each into a triangle and a parallelogram, effectively simplifying the problem by reducing it from one about trapezia to one about triangles.

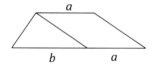

Let the triangle have perimeter p and area Δ and the trapezium have perimeter P and area A. Then

$$P = p + 2a,$$
$$A = \Delta + 2\left(\frac{a}{b}\right)\Delta = \left(\frac{2a+b}{b}\right)\Delta.$$

We need $P = A$, so

$$p + 2a = \left(\frac{2a+b}{b}\right)\Delta$$
$$(p + 2a)b = (2a + b)\Delta$$
$$pb + 2ab = 2a\Delta + b\Delta$$
$$2a(\Delta - b) = b(p - \Delta)$$
$$a = \frac{b(p - \Delta)}{2(\Delta - b)}.$$

Therefore, $p > \Delta$, and we seek triangles with integer sides satisfying this condition and check if a is an integer. There are three such triangles, the basic (3,4,5) and two isosceles triangles made up of two (3,4,5) triangles stuck together, the (5,5,6) and (5,5,8) triangles.

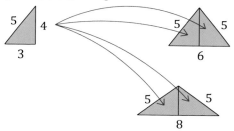

For the (3,4,5) triangle, $p = 12$ and $\Delta = 6$; so

$$a = \frac{b(p - \Delta)}{2(\Delta - b)} = \frac{6b}{2(6 - b)}.$$

If $b = 3$, then $a = 3$, and the associated trapezium has perimeter and area 18; if $b = 4$, then $a = 6$, and the trapezium has perimeter and area 24; and if $b = 5$, $a = 15$, the trapezium has perimeter and area 42.

For the (5,5,6) triangle, $p = 16$ and $\Delta = 12$; so

$$a = \frac{b(p - \Delta)}{2(\Delta - b)} = \frac{2b}{12 - b}.$$

If $b = 6$, then $a = 2$, and the associated trapezium has perimeter and area 20.

For the (5,5,8) triangle, $p = 18$ and $\Delta = 12$; so

$$a = \frac{b(p - \Delta)}{2(\Delta - b)} = \frac{3b}{12 - b}.$$

If $b = 8$, then $a = 6$, and the associated trapezium has perimeter and area 30.

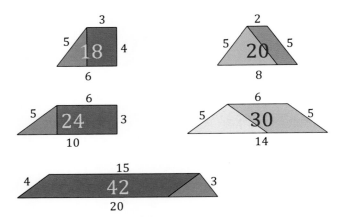

What about more complex polygons? Can we find say a pentagon with numerically equal perimeter and area, relaxing the condition that all sides are integers, if need be? The answer is that it can be achieved by scaling. Take as an example, what looks like the gable-end of a house (below). The gable on the left has $P = 30, A = 60$. So if we halve all lengths, the perimeter is reduced by a factor of 2 to 15 and the area reduced by a factor of $2^2 = 4$, taking it to 15 as well. Essentially, we are using a scale factor of ½.

In general, if we have a polygon with $P \neq A$, we imagine scaling by a factor k, so that the new perimeter and area are kP and k^2A. As we want these two measurements to be numerically equal, we set $kP = k^2A$. This gives the required scale factor as $k = P/A$. In effect, this is what we did in our gable example, the value of k being ½ in that case.

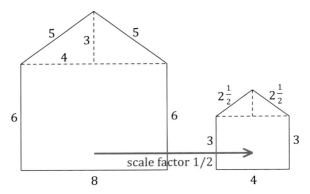

So we can take any polygon and scale it so that its perimeter and area are numerically equal. And an equivalent approach can be used with 3-dimensional figures, allowing volume and total surface area to become aligned numerically. Given a polyhedron with $A \neq V$, we again use a linear scale factor of k, so that the new surface area and volume are, respectively, k^2A and k^3V. Now we set $k^2A = k^3V$, which reduces to the scale factor $k = A/V$.

Take as an example, a cuboid of sides 2, 3 and 4 units.

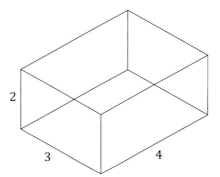

$A = 2(6 + 8 + 12) = 52.$
$V = 2 \times 3 \times 4 = 24.$
So $k = A/V = 13/6.$

Scaling by this linear factor produces a new cuboid of sides $13/3$, $13/2$ and $26/3$ which has the desired property (now $A = V = 2197/9$).

Now take some favourite 3-dimensional shapes. Let's start with the cylinder of radius r and height h.

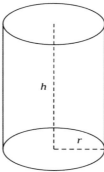

We have $A = 2\pi r^2 + 2\pi rh$, $V = \pi r^2 h$. If $A = V$, then

$$2\pi r^2 + 2\pi rh = \pi r^2 h$$
$$2r + 2h = rh$$
$$h(r - 2) = 2r$$
$$h = \frac{2r}{r - 2}.$$

If we restrict the values of r and h to positive integers, this gives three solutions:
$$r = 3, h = 6$$
$$r = h = 4$$
$$r = 6, h = 3.$$
The respective surface areas / volumes are 54π, 64π and 108π.

Similarly, if we equate the numerical values of the surface area and volume of a sphere, we get

$$4\pi r^2 = \frac{4}{3}\pi r^3$$
$$r^3 - 3r^2 = 0$$

$$r^2(r-3) = 0$$
$$r = 3.$$

There is just a single integer solution this time, with $A = V = 36\pi$.

Can you show that for an enclosed hemisphere, there is again a single solution, when $r = 9/2$? What about a cylinder surmounted by a hemisphere, the shape of a grain silo? Again a single solution, $r = h = 3$, yielding $A = V = 45\pi$.

Equable paths and frames

The figure below shows a path around a small triangular lawn. The dimensions of the lawn are 3 m, 4 m and 5 m, and those of the garden (lawn plus path) are 9 m, 12 m and 15 m, so both triangles are right-angled and in fact they are similar too. The width of the path is 2 m and the dotted lines show angle bisectors.

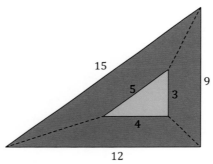

The total perimeter, P, of the path is the combined lengths of the edges on the left and right as we walk along it around the garden and back to where we started. So $P = (3 + 4 + 5) + (9 + 12 + 15) = 48$ m.

We may cut up the path into three trapezia and rearrange them to form a long trapezium, as shown below. This reorders the line segments in the perimeter but also reduces the labour required to find the area.

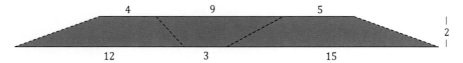

The area of the path, A, is found via either of the routes:

$$A = \tfrac{1}{2} \times 2(18 + 30) = 48 \text{ m}^2.$$
$$A = \tfrac{1}{2} \times 12 \times 9 - \tfrac{1}{2} \times 4 \times 3 = 48 \text{ m}^2.$$

P and A are numerically equal.

Here's a simpler case, a path 2 m wide around a square lawn of side 7 m.

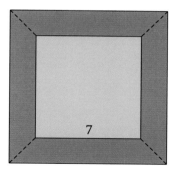

The side of the garden is 2 + 7 + 2 = 11 m.

$$P = 4 \times 7 + 4 \times 11 = 28 + 44 = 72.$$
$$A = 11^2 - 7^2 = 121 - 49 = 72.$$

Again, the perimeter and area are numerically equal.

Perhaps we see the results as pure coincidence. Or perhaps we start to develop a conjecture: when a path of width 2 m surrounds a lawn, its perimeter and area are numerically equal. At this point, a scientist would gather more examples of the same type (i.e. path width = 2 m) to bolster the evidence. A mathematician would perhaps do that too but if it turned up no counter-example, he or she would also seek a general proof.

The figures below are of a rectangular swimming pool, a flower garden in the shape of a regular hexagon and an L-shaped house (here seen in plan), each surrounded by a path of width 2 m. Do they add evidence to the conjecture or do they refute it?

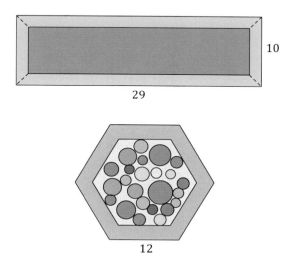

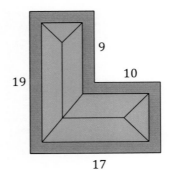

Swimming pool

$$P = 2(29 + 10) + 2(25 + 6) = 140.$$
$$A = 29 \times 10 - 25 \times 6$$
$$= 290 - 150$$
$$= 140.$$

Flower garden

Consider the left end of the isosceles trapezium at the bottom.

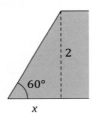

The width of the path is 2 m and the angle between the side and the line joining the outer and inner vertices is 60°. So $\tan 60° = 2/x$ and therefore $x = 2/\sqrt{3}$. The side of the inner hexagon is h, where:

$$h = 12 - 2x = 12 - \frac{4}{\sqrt{3}} = 12 - \frac{4}{3}\sqrt{3} = \frac{4}{3}(9 - \sqrt{3}).$$
$$P = 72 + 8(9 - \sqrt{3}) = 8(18 - \sqrt{3}).$$

As the hexagon is made up of 6 isosceles trapezia, its area is

$$A = 6 \times \frac{1}{2} \times 2 \left(24 - \frac{4}{3}\sqrt{3}\right) = 2(72 - 4\sqrt{3}) = 8(18 - \sqrt{3}).$$

L-shaped house

$$P = 2(17 + 19) + 2(13 + 15) = 128.$$
$$A = 19 \times 7 + 10 \times 10 - 15 \times 3 - 6 \times 10$$
$$= 133 + 100 - 45 - 60$$
$$= 128.$$

It is tempting to test whether a circle (a polygon with an infinite number of sides) also possesses this property. So here is a boating pond of diameter 16 m, enclosed by a 2 m path.

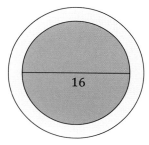

Boating pond

$$P = 20\pi + 16\pi = 36\pi.$$
$$A = 10^2\pi - 8^2\pi = 36\pi.$$

It doesn't take a lot of work to discover that if we change the width of the path, total perimeter and area are not numerically equal. Let's see how difficult it is to derive the special path width of 2 from the original shapes, at least in the case of the square, rectangle and circle.

First imagine that we have a square of side s, surrounded by a path of width w.

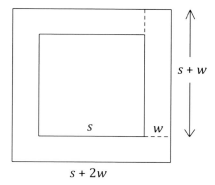

$P = 4(s + s + 2w) = 8(s + w)$.
$A = 4w(s + w)$.
So if $P = A$, then $4w = 8$ and $w = 2$.

Here is a rectangle with a bordering path of width w.

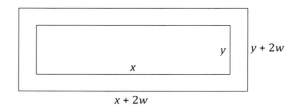

$P = 2(x + x + 2w) + 2(y + y + 2w) = 4(x + y + 2w).$
$A = 2w(x + w) + 2w(y + w) = 2w(x + y + 2w).$
If $P = A$, then $2w = 4$ and $w = 2$.

And the circle:

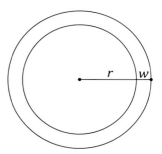

$P = 2r\pi + 2(r + w)\pi = 2(2r + w)\pi,$
$A = (r + w)^2\pi - r^2\pi = w(2r + w)\pi,$

and the result follows immediately.

Our conclusion is that if you want a closed-circuit path such that its total perimeter and its area are equal numerically, then ensure that the path has a width of 2 units. The result is given in more generality by Apostol and Mnatsakanian (2011). They invoke the concept of a 'frame', rather than our 'path'. Their result is that 'for any convex polygonal frame, its width w, area A, and total perimeter P are related by the equation

$$A = \frac{1}{2}Pw.'$$

Here, we have considered only the special case of $w = 2$, for which $A = P$. And despite referring to polygonal frames, the authors do provide a partially curvilinear example, which we might call the 'protractor' (a rectangle surmounted by a semi-annulus).

Can you establish the result that Apostol and Mnatsakanian state, that the total perimeter and the area are both given by $2\pi(r + 1) + 4(r + 2)$?

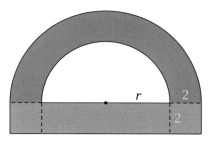

References

Apostol, T. M. & Mnatsakanian, M.A. 'Complete dissections: converting regions and their boundaries', *American Mathematical Monthly* 118, 9 (November 2011), pp. 789-798.

Palfreyman, M. 'Equable triangles – the general case', *SymmetryPlus* 57 (Summer 2015), pp. 5-7.

5   *Cyclic Quadrilaterals*

5.1 Introduction

Geometry is not well represented in the curriculum these days, though perhaps we should be pressing for this situation to be addressed. As teachers, most of us fall into one of two categories; those whose geometry is rusty, and those for whom there was never any geometrical metal to rust. What follows may appear frightening, but it could provide suitable enrichment for pupils, especially if they have access to a dynamic geometry software package such as *GeoGebra, Cabri, Desmos* or, as used here, *Geometer's Sketchpad*. Cyclic quadrilaterals were the subject of some articles I wrote for *Mathematics in School* and three more for the *SMC Journal*:

- 'Cyclic quadrilaterals: from generation to generation', *SMC Journal* 36 (2007), pp. 50-59.
- 'Another tour around the cyclic quadrilateral: Ptolemy and Van Schooten', *SMC Journal* 40 (2010), pp. 66-71.
- 'Brahmagupta, master of the cyclic quadrilateral', *SMC Journal* 41 (2011), pp. 69-71.

The material in this chapter comes from the first of these articles and the earlier parts of the second. So, if after reading it you wish to explore cyclic quadrilaterals some more, you can always check out what has not been included here because of the restrictions on space.

Take a circle, centre O, mark four points (A, B, C and D) at random on its circumference and join them up to produce $ABCD$. The shape created is a cyclic quadrilateral, the most interesting polygonal shape after the triangle.

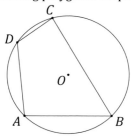

Cyclic quadrilaterals tend to produce more of their type when basic geometrical constructions are carried out on them. The cyclic quadrilateral species is maintained in a direct, 'father-to-son' line and also in a less direct, 'uncle-to-nephew' line from one generation to the next.

5.2 Prelude: triangle geometry

Though some of the most elementary and hence most useful properties of triangles are met in our courses, it may make some sense to reiterate them here and extend a little to associated properties. A line drawn from a vertex to a point on the opposite side (or opposite side extended) is called a *cevian*, which should be pronounced "chavian", since it is named after the Italian geometer, Giovanni Ceva (1647–1734). All but the third of the types of lines listed below are cevians. See Coxeter & Greitzer (1967, ch. 1), Rees (2003). Consider triangle *ABC* below.

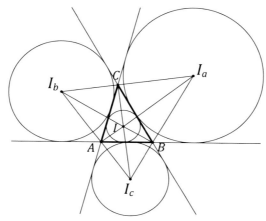

- *Interior angle bisectors* are concurrent at the *incentre, I*; the incentre is the centre of the *inscribed circle* or *incircle*, which has radius *r*.

- *Exterior angle bisectors* are concurrent at the *excentres, I_a, I_b, I_c*; the excentres are the centres of the *escribed circles* or *excircles*, which have radii r_a, r_b, r_c.

- *Perpendicular bisectors* of the sides are concurrent at the *circumcentre*, the centre of the *circumcircle, O*, which has radius *R*.

- *Medians*, drawn to the midpoints of the sides, are concurrent at the *centre of gravity* or *centroid, G*, and divide the triangle into six triangles of equal area.

- *Altitudes*, which meet the opposite sides at right-angles, are concurrent at the *orthocentre, H*.

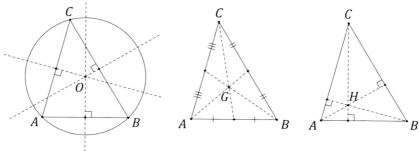

You may have detected evidence of one of the family traits of the triangle from the first diagram on the next page; namely, that the excentres form the vertices of a triangle $(I_a I_b I_c)$ which is similar to the original triangle, ABC. Perhaps this similarity is also a trait of cyclic quadrilaterals. We shall see.

5.3 Cyclic quadrilaterals: fundamental property

The most fundamental property of a cyclic quadrilateral is that its opposite angles (properly, alternating pairs of angles) are supplementary; that is, they sum to 180°. This result was first given by Euclid in Book III, Proposition 22 of his *Elements* and used in a small number of proofs thereafter.

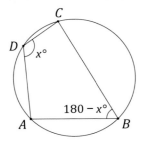 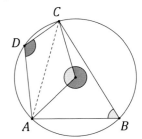

The theorem is easily proved by using the fact that the angle at the centre is twice the angle at the circumference. In the right-hand figure above, the angle shaded lightly at the centre is twice the size of the angle shaded lightly at the circumference; and similarly for the angles shaded darkly. The total angle size at the centre is 360°, so the opposite angles at the circumference sum to 180°.

One consequence of this result is that for cyclic quadrilaterals any exterior angle is equal to the opposite interior angle ($\angle CBE = \angle CDA$).

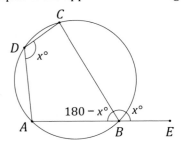 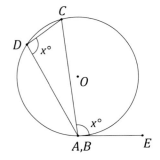

Imagine A and B approaching each other along the circumference whilst C and D remain fixed. When A and B eventually collide (i.e. coincide), chord AB is replaced by tangent AE. The cyclic quadrilateral has degenerated into $\triangle ACD$ with $\angle CAE = \angle CDA$ thereby providing a surprising demonstration of the alternate segment theorem of triangle geometry.

Classroom activity:
What types of quadrilateral can be cyclic?

- all squares and rectangles are cyclic;
- some shapes with a single axis of symmetry are cyclic (some kites and isosceles trapezia);
- all other cyclic quadrilaterals are irregular;
- no rhombus is cyclic (except the square) and no parallelogram (except the square and rectangle).

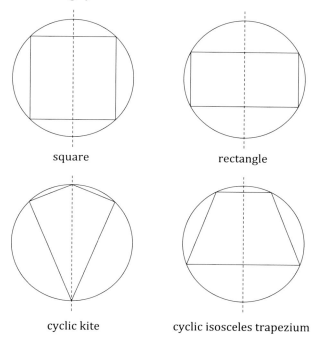

| square | rectangle |

| cyclic kite | cyclic isosceles trapezium |

Incidentally, there are seven cyclic quadrilaterals having sides of integer length (a, b, c, d) which are equable (see §4.6 of this book), though only two of the seven are irregular:

a	b	c	d	Perimeter	Area	Shape
4	4	4	4	16	16	square
6	6	3	3	18	18	kite
6	3	6	3	18	18	rectangle
8	5	5	2	20	20	irregular
8	5	2	5	20	20	isosceles trapezium
14	6	5	5	30	30	irregular
14	5	6	5	30	30	isosceles trapezium

5.4 Angle bisectors

Consider an irregular quadrilateral, $ABCD$, and draw its interior angle bisectors, AP, BP, CR and DR. These lines meet to form the vertices of a cyclic quadrilateral, $PQRS$, creating order out of chaos. The proof that $PQRS$ is cyclic is surprisingly straightforward.

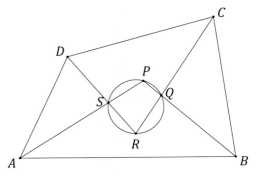

Let $\angle DAS = \angle SAB = \alpha$. Similarly, let $\angle ABQ = \angle QBC = \beta$, $\angle BCQ = \angle QCD = \gamma$ and $\angle CDS = \angle SDA = \delta$.

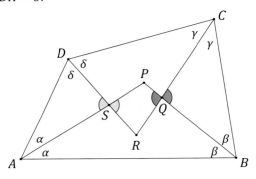

Note that $2\alpha + 2\beta + 2\gamma + 2\delta = 360°$, so $\alpha + \beta + \gamma + \delta = 180°$.

Also, $\angle PSR = \angle ASD = 180° - (\alpha + \delta)$,
$\qquad \angle RQP = \angle CQB = 180° - (\beta + \gamma)$.
So, $\quad \angle PSR + \angle RQP = 360° - (\alpha + \beta + \gamma + \delta) = 180°$.

If one pair of opposite angles of a quadrilateral are supplementary, so are the other pair and hence *PQRS* is cyclic.

What if the angle bisection is exterior? In the figure below, *ABCD* is a cyclic quadrilateral with its sides extended. The exterior angle bisectors meet at *W, X, Y* and *Z*, the centres of the escribed circles. *WXYZ* is a cyclic quadrilateral, and the proof proceeds as in the case of the interior angle bisectors.

Now that we know that when we carry out interior or exterior angle bisection on an arbitrary quadrilateral we produce an offspring quadrilateral that is cyclic, we might wonder what would happen if we repeat the process over and over. Clearly, the sons and daughters in one generation would have the cyclic characteristic of their parents but in what way would they differ? We could explore this numerically, and then add some algebra later. Let's begin with a parent cyclic quadrilateral with angles 50°, 60°, 130° and 120°.

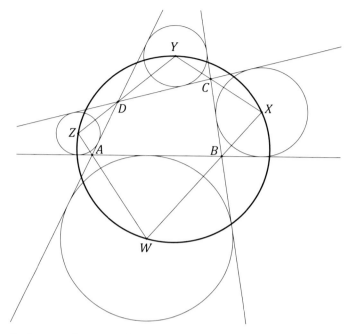

If the excircles are drawn and their centres joined then the offspring cyclic quadrilateral has angles 95°, 125°, 85° and 55° (as in the figure below, left). To see where we get these figures from, focus on the original cyclic quadrilateral and the triangle ADZ (below, right). The angles lying either side of the 120° angle at D are equal, a result of the angle bisection. So they are each ½ × 60° = 30°. Similarly, the angles neighbouring the 50° angle at A are each 65°. Hence, $\angle DZA = 180° - (30° + 65°) = 85°$. We can also think of this result as

$$\angle DZA = \angle YZW = 180° - \tfrac{1}{2}(60° + 130°),$$

where the angles in the bracket are the angles at B and C respectively.

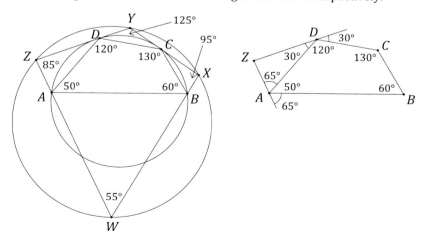

Similar calculations confirm the sizes of the other three angles of the offspring cyclic quadrilateral, *WXYZ*. So we can express the angles of the offspring in terms of the angles of the parent:

$$\angle YZW = 180° - \frac{1}{2}(60° + 130°) = 85°,$$

$$\angle ZWX = 180° - \frac{1}{2}(130° + 120°) = 55°,$$

$$\angle WXY = 180° - \frac{1}{2}(120° + 50°) = 95°,$$

$$\angle XYZ = 180° - \frac{1}{2}(50° + 60°) = 125°.$$

It also appears that as we move from generation to generation, some turning is taking place. We can continue quickly from generation to generation, as in the table below. It shows the angles in the parent cyclic quadrilateral (top row), in degrees, the angles in the offspring on the second row and so on for another five generations.

60		130		120		50		
	85		55		95		125	
75		**110**		105		70		
	87.5		**72.5**		92.5		107.5	
82.5		100		**97.5**		80		
	88.75		81.25		**91.25**		98.75	
86.25		95		93.75		**85**		
	89.375		85.625		90.625		**94.375**	

Note that without considering the rotation we get the angles on the diagonal (in bold font), which appear to have oscillatory convergence. If the rotation is taken into consideration, angles taken after an even number of applications of the process (in the columns) appear to converge to a limit either from above or from below according to the initial values chosen. The difference between an angle and the assumed limit of 90° is halved with each double application.

Let the angles of a cyclic quadrilateral be α_n, β_n, $180 - \alpha_n$ and $180 - \beta_n$, where n is the generation (the parent generation being $n = 0$). Then the angles of successive cyclic quadrilaterals produced by the angle bisection process are calculated using the linked recurrence relations:

$$\alpha_{n+1} = 180 - \frac{1}{2}(\alpha_n + \beta_n) \qquad (1)$$

$$\beta_{n+1} = 180 - \frac{1}{2}(\beta_n + 180 - \alpha_n)$$

$$= 90 - \frac{1}{2}(\beta_n - \alpha_n) \qquad (2)$$

Let the sequence of α_n approach the limit L_1 and the sequence of β_n approach the limit L_2.

Then (1) reduces to

$$L_1 = 180 - \frac{1}{2}(L_1 + L_2) \text{ or } 3L_1 - L_2 = 360 \qquad (1)'$$

and (2) reduces to

$$L_2 = 90 - \frac{1}{2}(L_2 - L_1) \text{ or } -L_1 + 3L_2 = 180 \qquad (2)'$$

Solving this pair of simultaneous equations gives $L_1 = L_2 = 90$. This confirms that the cyclic quadrilaterals in the sequence exhibit greater symmetry of form after each iteration, as the limiting rectangle is approached. In fact, the limiting form is a square. (The gist of what's going on with the sides is that at each iteration the length of a side is the average of a pair of adjacent sides scaled by a factor of $\sqrt{2}$. The justification for this statement requires some additional work which we will not include here.)

Before going any further, we should perhaps point out that as with the interior angle bisectors, the external angle bisectors of **all** quadrilaterals meet at the vertices of cyclic quadrilaterals.

5.5 Perpendicular bisectors

As with the triangle, when we construct the perpendicular bisectors of the sides of a cyclic quadrilateral, we find that they are concurrent (meet at a single point). That point is the centre of the circle on which the vertices lie. But as we shall see they also divide the original cyclic quadrilateral into four smaller quadrilaterals, which are also cyclic.

In the diagram below, *ABCD* is a cyclic quadrilateral lying on a circle with centre *O*. The perpendicular bisectors of *AB, BC, CD, DA* are *OM, ON, OP, OQ* respectively. These perpendicular bisectors meet at *O. OQAM, OMBN, ONCP, OPDQ* are all cyclic quadrilaterals.

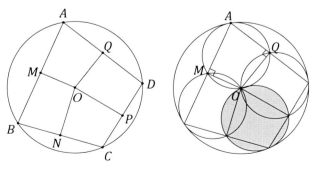

Proof

In $OQAM$, $OM \perp AM$ and $OQ \perp AQ$.

So $\angle OMA + \angle OQA = 180°$.

Hence $OQAM$ is a cyclic quadrilateral, and the proofs that the other quadrilaterals are cyclic follow in exactly the same manner.

Furthermore, the four small circles are congruent and their circumcentres form the vertices of another cyclic quadrilateral, $EFGH$. The circumcircle of $EFGH$ is also congruent to the four small circles. The common radius of the small circles is half that of the original circle through A, B, C and D. Indeed, $EFGH$ is a dilatation (here, a reduction) of $ABCD$, centre O, scale factor ½.

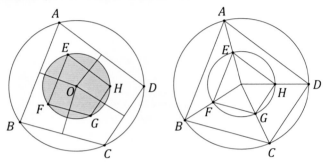

5.6 The five beer mats theorem

I cannot leave this section without mentioning a lovely theorem that comes from the same stable as the material we've covered so far. Four identical beer mats are placed on a table so that they intersect at a single point P. Common tangents drawn to adjacent mats meet at W, X, Y and Z on the edge of the plate, so that $WXYZ$ is a cyclic quadrilateral (see Honsberger, 1991, p. 36). Where is the fifth beer mat? Its edge passes through the centres of the other four beer mats.

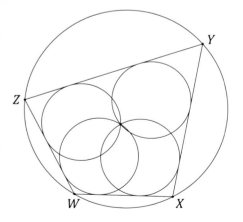

Proof

Let the centres of the four circles representing the beer mats be A, B, C, D respectively. Draw $ABCD$ and its circumcircle, centre P and note that $\angle DAK, \angle BAL, \angle BCM$ and $\angle DCN$ are all right angles.

Now let $\angle KWL = \alpha$. Then $\angle DAB = 360° - [(180° - \alpha) + 2 \times 90°] = \alpha$.
By a similar argument, $\angle BCD = 180° - \alpha$.

So *ABCD* is cyclic, and since its radius is equal to that of the other four circles, it is congruent to them. The edge of the fifth beer mat passes through the centres of the other four.

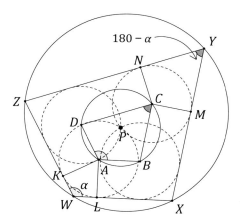

5.7 Maltitudes

The medians of a triangle are drawn from vertices to the midpoints of opposite sides and altitudes are drawn from vertices to meet opposite sides at right angles. In a cyclic quadrilateral there are no sides opposite a vertex, as such, and consequently, the concepts of median and altitude are meaningless. But there is an interesting mongrel: a line drawn from the midpoint of one side to meet the opposite side at right angles (*IE*, for example).

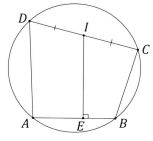
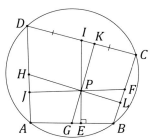

The accepted term for such a line is a 'maltitude', possibly a contraction of 'midpoint altitude', though probably first used as a contraction of 'median altitude' (Lester, 1962). If the four maltitudes are drawn, they do not lead us to another cyclic quadrilateral. In fact, they meet at a point.

To summarise, the father-to-son descent is present when we construct internal or external angle bisectors, though this is also the case even if the parent quadrilateral is not cyclic. As we have seen, the perpendicular bisection of the sides of a cyclic quadrilateral produces numerous offspring of the cyclic quadrilateral type. The four maltitudes, however, are concurrent.

5.8 Division into triangles

There is a rather indirect line of descent which yields many more lovely geometrical results. The starting points are not the cyclic quadrilaterals themselves but their component triangles. By drawing in a diagonal, a cyclic quadrilateral can be split into two triangles in two ways.

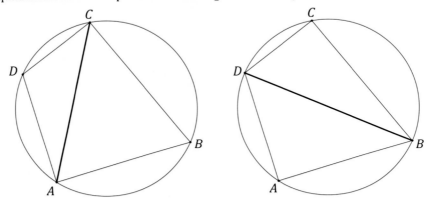

The centres of the four inscribed circles of the two pairs of triangles (E, F; G, H) form not only a cyclic quadrilateral but a rectangle, *EGFH*.

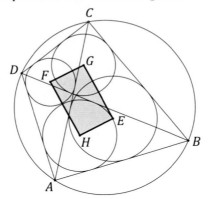

For a proof, see the website of the late, great Antonio Gutierrez. There, and elsewhere (Pritchard, 2003, pp. 274-279), Gutierrez also repackages the result as the 'Eyeball Theorem'. Alternatively, refer to Michael de Villiers' book *Some Adventures in Euclidean Geometry*, p. 190.

There is the interesting special case of the cyclic kite. Since it has an axis of bilateral symmetry, adjacent sides of the rectangle are equal, and hence *EGFH* is a square, and its diagonals, *FE* and *GH* are equal.

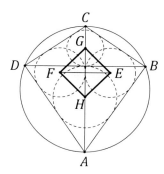

If we separate out the pairs of triangles, we can see clearly that the sum of the radii of the two inscribed circles on the left is equal to the sum of the radii of the circles on the right. No surprise there!

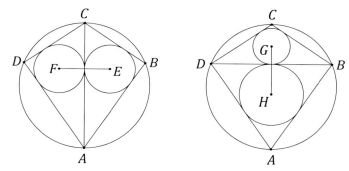

But if we lose the axis of symmetry for a moment, and return to the general cyclic quadrilateral, the result still holds.

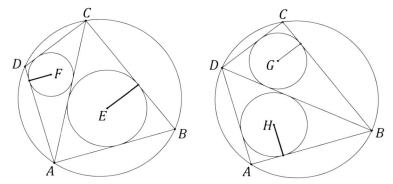

This may be called the Cyclic Quadrilateral Sangaku Theorem. It was postulated about 1800, and can be proved using Carnot's Theorem (see the original article in *SMC Journal* 36). It is a special case of the Sangaku Theorem: If a cyclic polygon is divided into triangles by drawing non-intersecting diagonals, the sum of the radii of the inscribed triangles is the same regardless of how the division is carried out. Here are some of the configurations for a cyclic hexagon:

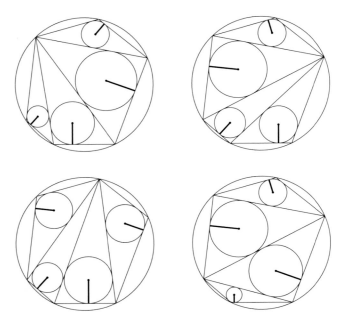

In Japan, decorative wooden tablets or 'sangaku' were traditionally hung in Buddhist temples and Shinto shrines. From about 1680 onwards, many of these tablets bore geometric problems or theorems and the name of the supplying mathematician. The custom developed that other mathematicians would attempt to supply the proofs, and among the most adept were Seki Kōwa (1642–1708), Ajima Chokuen, or Naonobu (1732–1798), and Shoto Kenmotu (1790–1871). Roughly 900 sangaku have survived to this day. Many of the problems have been interpreted by Fukagawa Hidetoshi, a secondary school teacher, and published in English in association with geometers Daniel Pedoe (Hidetoshi & Pedoe, 1989) and Tony Rothman (Hidetoshi & Rothman, 2008). The latter book, *Sacred Mathematics: Japanese Temple Geometry*, is particularly beautiful. There is also further accessible material on sangaku in Chapter 6 of *The Room in the Elephant* (Pritchard, 2019).

5.9 Ptolemy's Theorem

Now we consider the wonderful theorem of Ptolemy and its association with the addition formulas and double-angle formulas of trigonometry. Claudius Ptolemy (c.85 – c.165 CE) was the most influential astronomer of the ancient world. It is after him that the author of the Ptolemaic or earth-centred system of the universe is named. His *Almagest* or *Collection* (written about 150 CE) contains the statement and proof of the theorem now named after him:

> The rectangle contained by the diagonals of any quadrilateral inscribed in a circle is equal to the sum of the rectangles contained by the pairs of opposite sides.

We may write this in more modern form as:

In a cyclic quadrilateral, the product of the diagonals is equal to the sum of the products of the opposite sides, or $AC.BD = AB.CD + AD.BC$.

Proof

First construct E on AC such that $\angle EDA = \angle CDB$.

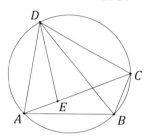

$\angle CAD = \angle CBD$ (both subtended by the same chord, CD).

So $\triangle AED$ is similar to $\triangle BCD$ (equal angles), corresponding sides in fixed ratio.

In particular, $\quad \dfrac{AE}{BC} = \dfrac{AD}{BD} \quad \Rightarrow \quad AE.BD = AD.BC \qquad\qquad (3)$

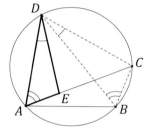 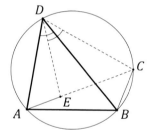

Now consider triangles ABD and ECD.

$\angle BDA = \angle CDE$ ($\angle EDA + \angle BDE$ and $\angle CDB + \angle BDE$ respectively).

So $\triangle ABD$ is similar to $\triangle ECD$ (equal angles) and again corresponding sides are in proportion.

In particular, $\quad \dfrac{EC}{AB} = \dfrac{CD}{BD} \quad \Rightarrow \quad EC.BD = AB.CD \qquad\qquad (4)$

Now add (3) and (4): $(AE + EC)BD = AB.CD + AD.BC$

Hence $\qquad\qquad\qquad\qquad AC.BD = AB.CD + AD.BC$

5.10 Sine rule, and the addition and double-angle formulas

We can use Ptolemy's Theorem in conjunction with the Sine Rule to establish the addition formulas and the double-angle formulas for sine and cosine (see Maor, 1998), though there is space here for only the formulas for sine.

These days we tend to use the Sine Rule in a form divorced from its roots in pure geometry. The extended theorem states that for the general triangle, ABC:

$$\frac{a}{\sin A} = \frac{b}{\sin B} = \frac{c}{\sin C} = 2R,$$

where R is the radius of the circumcircle.

Proof

$\triangle ABC$ is inscribed in a circle, centre O. D is on the circumference, so that BD is a diameter, of length $2R$ (left figure).

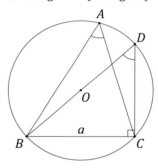 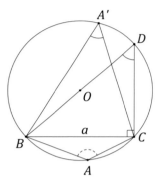

$\angle BCD = 90°$ (angle in a semicircle) and $\angle CDB = \angle CAB$ (same segment, BC).

So $\sin D = \dfrac{a}{2R} = \sin A \quad \Rightarrow \quad \dfrac{a}{\sin A} = 2R.$

Similarly, $\dfrac{b}{\sin B} = 2R$ and $\dfrac{c}{\sin C} = 2R.$

For the case where $\angle A$ is obtuse, locate the vertex A on minor arc BC. $ACA'B$ is a cyclic quadrilateral and hence $\sin A = \sin(180° - A') = \sin A'$ and the relationship with $2R$ is as before.

The Sine Rule, as we normally quote it, is revealed by taking the particular case of the circle having unit diameter:

$$\frac{a}{\sin A} = \frac{b}{\sin B} = \frac{c}{\sin C} = 1.$$

Also following from this relationship are $a = \sin A$, $b = \sin B$, $c = \sin C$.

In the figure below, $WXYZ$ is a quadrilateral inscribed in a circle, centre O, with diameter $WY = 1$. Let $\angle ZWY = \alpha$, $\angle YWX = \beta$, so that $\angle ZWX = \alpha + \beta$ and note that $\angle WXY = \angle YZW = 90°$ (angles in a semicircle).

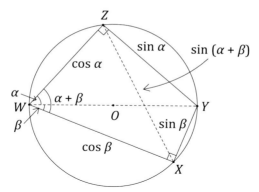

By the Sine Rule, $XZ = \sin(\alpha + \beta)$.

By Ptolemy's Theorem: $XZ.WY = YZ.WX + ZX.XY$ and by making the substitutions for these lengths, the addition formula for sine drops out:

$$\sin(\alpha + \beta) = \sin \alpha \cos \beta + \cos \alpha \sin \beta.$$

Now reflect X in the diameter WY, its image being X'.

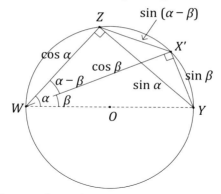

By the Sine Rule, $X'Z = \sin(\alpha - \beta)$.

By Ptolemy's Theorem:

$$ZY.X'W = X'Z.WY + ZW.YX'$$

$$\sin \alpha \cos \beta = \sin(\alpha - \beta) + \cos \alpha \sin \beta$$

$$\sin(\alpha - \beta) = \sin \alpha \cos \beta - \cos \alpha \sin \beta.$$

The double-angle formula for sine comes from taking $\alpha = \beta$. Geometrically, this means taking the symmetric case in which the featured figure is a cyclic kite.

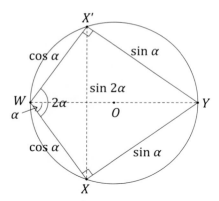

Ptolemy's Theorem gives $1 \times \sin 2\alpha = \sin \alpha \cos \alpha + \sin \alpha \cos \alpha$,

$$\sin 2\alpha = 2 \sin \alpha \cos \alpha.$$

References

Coxeter, H. S. M. & Greitzer, S. L. *Geometry Revisited*, Mathematical Association of America, MAA, 1967.

De Villiers, M. *Some Adventures in Euclidean Geometry*, University of Durban Westville, 1996.

Gutierrez, A. *GoGeometry* website at www.gogeometry.com

___ 'Eyeball Theorems', in Pritchard (2003), pp. 274-279.

Hidetoshi, F. & Pedoe, D. *Japanese Temple Geometry Problems*, Winnipeg: Charles Babbage Research Centre, 1989.

Hidetoshi, F. & Rothman, T. *Sacred Mathematics: Japanese Temple Geometry*, Princeton University Press, 2008.

Honsberger, R. *More Mathematical Morsels*, MAA / CUP, 1991.

Lester, R. E. 'The maltitudes of a cyclic quadrilateral', *Mathematical Gazette* Vol. 46, no. 356 (May 1962), p. 147.

Maor, E. *Trigonometric Delights*, Princeton University Press, 1998.

Pritchard, C. (ed.) *The Changing Shape of Geometry*, CUP/MAA, 2003.

___ *The Room in the Elephant*, Mathematical Association, 2019.

Rees, E. 'Ceva's Theorem', in Pritchard (2003), pp.187-188.

6   *History of Mathematics*

6.1 Christopher Wren and the Cycloid

SMC Journal 53 (2023), p. 61

A little birdie told me … that Christopher Wren was not only an architect but also a mathematician.

By the third century BCE, many of the properties of the conic sections – circle, ellipse, parabola and hyperbola – and of at least one spiral had been discovered, in the main by Euclid, Archimedes and Apollonius of Perga. But for a millennium and a half thereafter, curves that fall outside these families were either not known or they had been encountered but their properties were largely uncharted.

Then, in the period before the invention of the calculus by Isaac Newton and Gottfried Leibniz in the mid- to late-seventeenth century, the study of curves became a real focus for mathematicians. They studied curves such as the cycloid, cardioid, tautochrone, involute and brachistochrone, their focus being primarily on two questions, 'How long are they?' and 'What is the area under them?', problems they referred to as *rectification* (straightening and measuring) and *quadrature* (counting the little squares they enclose). In relation to Christopher Wren we need look at just one of those curves, the cycloid.

The cycloid is a curve generated by taking a circle or a circular object such as a wheel, making a mark on the circumference or rim, *P*, and rolling the circle along a straight line. The path traced out by the mark on the rim is a cycloid.

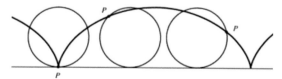

Christopher Wren (1632–1723) graduated from Oxford in 1651 (and with MA, 1653) and such was his brilliance that he became Gresham Professor of Astronomy as early as 1657 while still in his twenties. By this time, Galileo had found the quadrature of the cycloid (at least approximately) by tracing the curve onto a sheet of metal of uniform thickness, cutting out the piece and comparing its weight with that of the generating circle cut from the same sheet. His result that the area is three times that of the generating circle, i.e. $3\pi r^2$ was confirmed mathematically by Gilles de Roberval and conveyed to Marin Mersenne in 1634, though publication was held back until 1693.

Wren had just been installed as Gresham Professor when in 1658 he solved the *rectification* of the cycloid and asked Blaise Pascal (he of Pascal's triangle fame) to confirm his result. Wren's proof that the arc length is eight times the radius of the generating circle was published by the Savilian Professor of Geometry, John Wallis (1616–1703), in *Tractatus Duo* (1659), with Wren's priority clearly assigned.

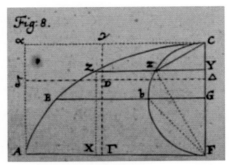

It might be expected that the result would feature π but the fact that it's just 8*r*, simple and rational, is indeed a surprise. It's so striking, in fact, that when the artist Robert Streater came to depict some of Christopher Wren's achievements on the ceiling of the Sheldonian Theatre in Oxford, he included the diagram of Wren's proof in one of the panels.

6.2 Archimedes' Tangrams
SMC Journal 48 (2018), pp. 49-51, and *SMC Primary Journal* 3 (2019), pp. 21-22

The Archimedes palimpsest

In 1906, one of the greatest discoveries in the history of mathematics was made. Johan Ludvig Heiberg, then the leading authority on the works of Archimedes, came across a palimpsest in the form of a tenth-century manuscript overwritten (in 1229, and probably in Jerusalem) with a prayer book. In such times, sourcing animal skins on which to write was not always easy and the surface text of a skin would be recycled by scraping it again – that's the meaning of 'palimpsest' – and a new text would be applied on top.

In recent years, the palimpsest has been housed in the Walters Art Museum in Baltimore where the writings of Archimedes have been recovered using imaging technology, and historians including Raviel Netz have contributed scholarly and popular commentaries. (See Netz, R. & Noel, W., *The Archimedes Codex: Revealing the Blueprint of Modern Science*, Phoenix, 2008.)

The Archimedes Palimpsest
Image: archimedespalimpsest.org

The palimpsest contains seven works by Archimedes and six by other writers. Those by Archimedes are,

- *The Equilibrium of Planes*
- *Spiral Lines*
- *The Measurement of the Circle*
- *Sphere and Cylinder*
- *On Floating Bodies*
- *The Method of Mechanical Theorems*
- *Stomachion*

The first four works have been known in the West for several centuries, but not so the last three and that makes them especially important. The hydrostatics text, *On Floating Bodies*, is the only version in Greek, the language in which Archimedes wrote it. Archimedes' *Method* includes an explanation of how to calculate areas and volumes by 'weighing' one shape against another, an approach which has been seen as an early and significant step towards integration. When Heiberg revealed this in the early twentieth century, we saw for the first time how Archimedes proved that the volume of a sphere is 2/3 of the volume of the surrounding cyclinder. The *Method* became the primary focus of everyone's attention and the *Stomachion* was largely ignored.

The word 'stomachion' means 'relating to the stomach' and it was often used in classical texts in the sense of a 'stomach ache'. But the ancient Greeks saw their stomachs as the seat of troublesome problems, so their use of the word is equivalent to our use of the word 'headache' when not referring literally to a pain in the head but figuratively to a difficulty to be overcome. In short, the puzzle was designed to provide a mental challenge.

Even though the fragment of the Stomachion came to be known so late, sets of the pieces made of ivory were in common use around the Mediterranean, and texts from antiquity refer to their being used by children. There were two challenges, the first being to form a square from them once they had been mixed up, which is clearly designed to develop spatial awareness. The second was to use the pieces to design figures resembling things in the real world, an opportunity to develop creative talents.

Archimedes' 14-piece Stomachion is shown below (left), and beside that an 11-piece variant proposed in modern times by George Miller and called simply the 'Stomach'. Miller's tangram is formed from the Stomachion by melding 4a and 4b into one piece, and similarly for 5a and 5b, and for 6a and 6b.

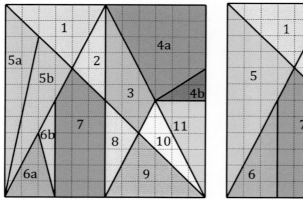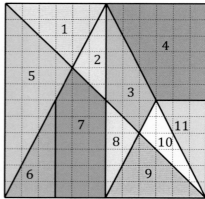

Archimedes' 'Stomachion' (left) and Miller's 'Stomach' (right)

Areas of the pieces

In the figure on the next page, the white pieces are all triangular. For each of them the base and vertical height can be seen immediately from the grid. As a result, calculating their areas is routine. To calculate the areas of the pieces coloured red, it is necessary to either add two or more areas together or to take one area from another, so it presents more of a challenge.

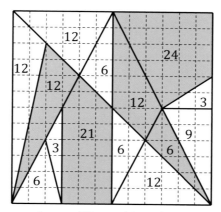

Areas of Stomachion pieces

Take piece 4a with area 24 as an example. Let's turn it around through 90° anticlockwise. Do we see it as a sum or as a difference of areas? In the figures below, we find the area of piece 4a (i.e. 24) as:

- 6 + 6 + 12
- 6 + 18
- 6 + 9 + 9
- 9 + 15
- 36 − 12

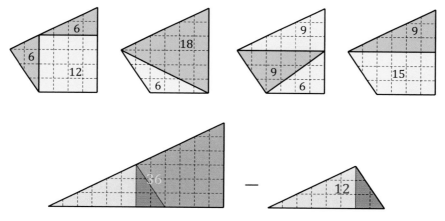

Piece 4a seen as an amalgamation of regions (4 variants),
or as the difference between two regions

Archimedes noted that the areas of all his pieces bar one can be expressed as unit fractions of the whole square. That piece is the red pentagon (piece 7), since 21 is the only area magnitude which does not divide 144, the area of the 12 by 12 square. He gave this fraction as

$$\frac{1}{2} \times \frac{1}{6} + \frac{1}{2} \times \frac{1}{8}.$$

163

Now the common denominator is 48, so Archimedes was visualising the tangram in blocks of 3 units (since $144 \div 48 = 3$). This leads to a possible task for today, that of dividing up not just the whole square into areas of 3 units but each piece separately. One such solution is:

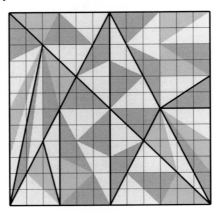

One lesson to be learnt from such an activity is that triangles with the same vertical height and lying on bases of equal length have the same area (even if they are obtuse). In practice, it takes longer to recognise how to proceed with the skinny pieces, more straightforward with the stockier pieces.

Boxing clever

Unfortunately, the Archimedes palimpsest contains only the first page of his *Stomachion*. The other pages were never included, probably because they were already damaged, and even that first-page fragment is in particularly poor condition. Nevertheless, Netz believes that it is all that remains of a very early example of a work on combinatorics. Archimedes had a passing interest in the areas of the pieces and no interest at all in creating shapes other than the original square from the pieces. He was simply boxing clever, trying to find all the ways of arranging the fourteen pieces into a square if we do not allow copies arising through reflection or rotation, a number we now know to be 536.

Although Archimedes clearly had loftier aims, youngsters still enjoy playing creatively with tangrams to this day, and one of the shapes that can be made from the fourteen pieces of the *Stomachion* is Archimedes' elephant.

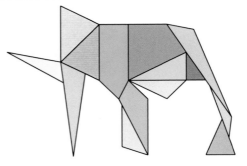

6.3 John Mair's Recipe Book

6.3.1 New introduction

When we think of the Scottish Enlightenment, several figures spring to mind – the philosophers, Adam Smith and David Hume; the neoclassical architect, Robert Adam; literary giants such as Robert Burns and Sir Walter Scott; the father of modern geology, James Hutton; the scientist Joseph Black and the mathematician Colin Maclaurin. But if these men were representative of the real pioneers of the period, there is a second tier of lesser-known figures who also played an important role; among them is John Mair (1702/1703–1769). This is the story of the man and his arithmetic textbook.

Mair was born and raised near the Falkland Estate in Fife and graduated from his local university, St Andrews, in 1726. He was drawn to teaching and gained a position at the Grammar School in Ayr at the second attempt. (At his first interview and examination held over three days, he was judged the equal of the other candidate except for the quality of his handwriting.) Here he would earn 200 merks per annum, the 'merk' (originally a silver coin) being worth two-thirds of a 'pound Scots'. The excellence of his teaching was matched by his enthusiasm for curriculum design and the writing of textbooks. His manual on accounting, *Book-keeping Methodiz'd*, became the standard text on the subject both in Britain and in North America for half a century after its initial publication in 1736, passing through eight editions in Mair's lifetime and a further nine editions after his death. Indeed, George Washington had a copy in his library at Mount Vernon. (Viewed in conjunction with the accounting texts written by three other Scots of this period, Alexander Malcolm, William Gordon and Robert Hamilton, the term the Scottish Ascendancy has been used to describe Scotland's preeminent position in developments in accountancy during the eighteenth century.)

The accountancy book is not the only thing for which John Mair is noted, for in 1761 he became a head teacher and not just any head teacher. Remember that he had already taken a keen interest in what a modern curriculum should look like. That vision was for an 'academy', an establishment for those youngsters whose parents could not afford for them to go to university, where English rather than Latin would be the vector of learning and where the range of subjects would reflect developments in the world of trade and industry. The school which Mair founded and then led was the first Academy in Scotland, Perth Academy. It was a model that was soon copied around the country. As well as leading his school, John Mair taught arithmetic, book-keeping and other sciences, and where there were no adequate texts within his own subjects or beyond, he simply sat down and wrote them, and then rewrote them. The list of his texts is stunning (see Michael Mepham, 1988, for details); books on Roman history, Latin, world geography, and of course book-keeping and arithmetic, with editions produced with metronomic regularity in Edinburgh, Glasgow and Dublin, and in Baltimore, Philadelphia and New York.

The focus of this chapter is John Mair's time in Perth and in particular his *Arithmetic*, but before we get there we should note that in 1751, while still at the Grammar School in Ayr, Mair had taken the first steps towards writing such a book by revising and correcting *Cocker's Arithmetic*. At the time, Edward Cocker's book was the standard text in English and was deemed so authoritative that the phrase 'according to Cocker' was often appended to a statement to assert its truth. John Mair took a different view, acknowledging that although the book is held in 'high esteem', it 'has nevertheless had the misfortune, for a long time past, to have been very carelessly printed; all the modern impressions, without exception, so much abounding in omissions, false figures, erroneous answers, and typographical blunders of every sort, that the book in many places tends to mislead or puzzle rather than instruct the learner'. (The image is of another Edinburgh edition of 1762.) Mair was not satisfied that *Cocker's Arithmetic* was suitable for his new Academy in Perth and so set about writing his own *Arithmetic*.

References

Mepham, M. J. 'The Scottish Enlightenment and the development of accounting', *The Accounting Historians Journal* 15, 2 (1988), pp. 151-176.

Mepham, M. J. & Stone, W. E. 'John Mair, M.A.: Author of the first classic book-keeping series', *Accounting and Business Research* 7, 26 (1977), pp. 128-134.

6.3.2 An old recipe book
Scottish Mathematical Council Journal 17 (1987), pp. 39-46

While browsing in a secondhand bookshop in Stromness, I spotted a fourth edition of John Mair's *Arithmetic*, published in Edinburgh in 1786. Its six-hundred and fifteen octavo pages were still in excellent condition and the original calf-skin binding was intact. The price? – a very reasonable £7. So it was that I began investigating a two-hundred-year-old recipe book, for that was what it turned out to be. On the way I gained some understanding of what constituted an education in arithmetic in Scotland in the second half of the eighteenth century.

John Mair had been 'Rector of the Academy at Perth' when he had written the original edition of the *Arithmetic*. The rector (i.e. in 1987), Mr James Waite, kindly sent me information about Mair and the establishment of Perth Academy in 1761. Clearly, the setting up of this new school – the first Academy in Scotland – constitutes a major event in the history of education in this country for never before had a school offered an education in English to those who were preparing for life as merchants, mechanics and farmers. Traditionally, schools had fulfilled a very different role – the preparation of aspiring lawyers, doctors and clerics for university. Indeed, the Rev. James Bonnar in a report to Perth Town Council in 1760 had noted that "in times not long past, all learning was made to consist of grammatical knowledge of dead languages, and skill in metaphysical subtleties, while what had an immediate reference to life and practice was despised." In contrast, the curriculum of Perth Academy was to be heavily weighted towards the sciences. During the first of a two-year course, pupils would concentrate almost exclusively on the mathematical subjects of algebra, arithmetic, Euclidean geometry and plain and spherical trigonometry and their applications in commerce, surveying, fortification, navigation and astronomy.

Of the two masters employed to teach at Perth Academy, little need be said about Dr John Tait save that he "lacked both the temperament and the training necessary" to be a successful teacher and resigned within a year of taking up his position when offered a surprisingly generous golden handshake of 100 guineas. John Mair, on the other hand, might be described as having been a 'natural' teacher in that he was able to take the most complex of subjects and simplify them so that his pupils could learn with facility. He died prematurely in 1769 but his *Arithmetic* proved popular for some years after his death.

The title page of Mair's book, leaves little doubt that the approach to be taken is Euclidean. There is no place here for modern zetetics; rather, the scrupulous detail of the axiomatic method. The axioms or first principles reduce to nine:

1. Any given number may be increased or diminished at pleasure, for there is no number so great, but a greater may be given, nor is there any number so small, but a smaller may be assigned.
2. Ten in an inferior place makes one or unit in the next higher place, and the reverse.
3. A number, by having one, two, three etc ciphers annexed to it becomes ten, a hundred, thousand etc times greater.
4. Any number is naturally resolved into as many constituent parts as it has significant features, by annexing to each significant figure as many ciphers as there are in figures on its right hand.
5. An unit is an aliquot part of every whole number and every whole number is a multiple of unity.
6. Numbers equally augmented or diminished continue to have the same difference.
7. The difference of two unequal numbers added to the lesser gives a sum equal to the greater; or subtracted from the greater leaves remainder equal to the lesser.
8. None but similar or like things can be added or subtracted.
9. Any whole is equal to its parts.

ARITHMETIC,

RATIONAL AND PRACTICAL:

WHEREIN

The Properties of NUMBERS are clearly pointed out ; the THEORY
of the Science deduced from firſt Principles ; the Methods of
OPERATION demonſtratively explained ; and the whole reduced
to PRACTICE in a great variety of uſeful RULES.

CONSISTING OF THREE PARTS, *viz.*

I. VULGAR ARITHMETIC.
II. DECIMAL ARITHMETIC.
III. PRACTICAL ARITHMETIC.

By JOHN MAIR, A.M.

RECTOR OF THE ACADEMY AT PERTH.

THE FOURTH EDITION.

EDINBURGH:
Printed for JOHN BELL and WILLIAM CREECH;
And ſold by T. LONGMAN, G. G. J. & J. ROBINSON, T. CADELL,
C. DILLY, and RICHARDSON & URQUHART, LONDON.

M.DCC.LXXXVI.

The title page of my copy of John Mair's *Arithmetic* (Fourth Edition, 1786)

Using these nine building blocks a carefully constructed arithmetic of the integers, vulgar fractions and decimals is developed in no less than 354 pages, before the applications are tackled, many in great depth. Dull and dreary? Not at all, for there is much here to catch the eye, especially the mathematical terminology, some of which is of Mair's invention. Borrowing liberally from the Greek rather than the Latin, Mair uses *tetragon* and *hexahedron* for square and cube, labels polygons of nine and eleven sides *enneagons* and *hendecagons* respectively and even plumps for *chiliad* in preference to millennium. Area questions are dealt with under the heading of *superficial measure*, the word volume is replaced by *solidity*, fractions are charmingly described as *broken numbers*, the adjectives *net* and *neat* are freely interchanged, reminding us thereby of the original meaning of net in such terms as net weight and net pay, and throughout the book the word *cipher*, assuming its literal meaning, replaces zero. Mathematical terminology remained rather fluid well into the nineteenth century, so it is hardly surprising that Mair should coin his own word, *parallelopleuron*, for what we now call a trapezium, nor that this word was stillborn, no other writer adopting it and the compilers of the thirteen-volume Oxford English Dictionary failing to give it recognition.

Of the four sections of Mair's book which particularly attracted my attention, the first highlights the need for a check on calculations and gives one quick method for effecting such a check; the next two give recipes for solving simple linear equations and extracting roots and the last shows how what is a fascinating algorithm in its own right could be used as a starting point for developing non-algorithmic strategies.

Casting out nines

Before electronic calculators were invented it was essential when carrying out laborious calculations to incorporate checking procedures. The most straightforward of them made use of inverse operations. Addition was checked by subtraction and *vice versa*, and likewise for multiplication and division, and for finding powers and extracting roots. The major disadvantage was that a tedious division such as $95.4327563275 \div 3.4637528$, which appears in the *Arithmetic*, needed to be checked using an equally tedious multiplication. The best checks were those which could be made quickly and with ease. By 1786, methods of checking using remainders (though not the theory of congruences on which they depend) had been used for quite some time. The simplest of them and the one favoured by Mair for checking addition, subtraction, and multiplication is known as 'casting out nines'. Since all non-negative powers of ten leave a remainder of 1 upon division by 9 and since division is distributive over addition, the remainder when any number is divided by 9 can be quickly found by adding up its digits and casting out nines i.e. subtracting multiples of 9. (Incidentally, our common test for divisibility is a special case of this result.) The placing of the check digits around a diagonal cross was, in Mair's day, the standard method of laying out the workings. In the examples that follow, all are modulo 9.

$$
\begin{array}{r}
347 \\
+\ 684 \\
\hline
1031
\end{array}
$$

$$
\begin{aligned}
3 + 4 + 7 &\equiv 5 \\
6 + 8 + 4 &\equiv 0
\end{aligned} \Big\} \ \text{sum} = 5
$$
$$
1 + 0 + 3 + 1 \equiv 5
$$

$$
\begin{array}{r}
5847 \\
-\ 2569 \\
\hline
3278
\end{array}
$$

$$
\begin{aligned}
5 + 8 + 4 + 7 &\equiv 6 \\
2 + 5 + 6 + 9 &\equiv 4 \\
3 + 2 + 7 + 8 &\equiv 2
\end{aligned} \Big\} \ \text{sum} = 6
$$

$$
\begin{array}{r}
754 \\
\times\ \ \ 38 \\
\hline
6032 \\
2262 \\
\hline
28652
\end{array}
$$

$$
7 + 5 + 4 \equiv 7
$$
$$
3 + 8 \equiv 2
$$
$$
\begin{array}{r}
7 \times 2 \equiv 5 \\
\hline
2 + 8 + 6 + 5 + 2 \equiv 5
\end{array}
$$

Of course, this checking procedure is not foolproof. In the subtraction example above, if the 8 and the 4 were carelessly transposed, giving 5487, or if the number to be subtracted was written down as 2560 then there would be no change to the remainders and consequently these errors would probably go unnoticed. Nevertheless, the method of casting out nines and to a lesser extent, that of casting out elevens were, not so long ago, both popular and necessary.

Rule of false

Under the heading of 'Rule of False' there are two algorithms called by Mair 'single position' and 'double position'. The former appears in the ancient Rhind papyrus (c.1650 BCE) and is retained today as the standard recipe for sharing in a given ratio.

Known to the Arabs as *elchataieym*, the rule of double false position was introduced into Europe by Leonardo of Pisa (Fibonacci) at the beginning of the thirteenth century. As an arithmetical routine it is of intrinsic interest, but the fact that it was necessary for Mair to include it in his textbook is of major significance. Here we have evidence that, even as late as 1786, the teaching of algebra was in its infancy. The first example given is:

A, B and C build a house, which cost £76; whereof A paid a sum unknown, B paid £10 more than A, and C paid as much as A and B. What did each partner pay?

		£				£
Position 1	A	6		Position 2	A	9
	B	16			B	19
	C	22			C	28
	Result	44			Result	56
		76				76
Error of defect		−32		Error of defect		−20

Pos.	Er.			£
6 ×	20 = 120		A	14
6 ×	32 = 288		B	24
	12) 168 (14		C	38
				76 proof

It should be noted that had Position 2 been

	£
A	16
B	26
C	42
Result	84

giving an error of excess of £8, then it would have been necessary to add both the errors and the cross-products of position and error, rather than subtract, thus:

Pos.	Er.
6 ×	8 = 48
16 ×	32 = 512
	40) 560 (14 etc

How does the algorithm work? Double position is a technique for solving simple linear equations: in this case A pays £x towards the building costs and the equation is $4x - 56 = 0$. In general, if the equation is $ax + b = 0$ (with solution $x = -b/a$) and if the two positions taken are $x = p_1$ and $x = p_2$, then

$$\left.\begin{array}{l}(1)\quad ap_1 + b = c_1 \\ (2)\quad ap_2 + b = c_2\end{array}\right\}\quad (c_1, c_2 \neq 0, \text{since the positions are false})$$

Subtracting: $a(p_2 - p_1) = c_2 - c_1$

whence

$$a = \frac{c_2 - c_1}{p_2 - p_1}.$$

Also, by multiplying (1) by p_2 and (2) by p_1, we have

$$ap_1 p_2 + bp_2 = c_1 p_2$$
$$ap_1 p_2 + bp_1 = c_2 p_1$$

Subtracting: $b(p_2 - p_1) = c_1 p_2 - c_2 p_1$

So $b = \dfrac{c_1 p_2 - c_2 p_1}{p_2 - p_1}.$

Hence, $x = -\dfrac{b}{a} = \dfrac{(c_1 p_2 - c_2 p_1)(p_2 - p_1)}{(p_2 - p_1)(c_1 - c_2)} = \dfrac{c_1 p_2 - c_2 p_1}{c_1 - c_2}, \quad c_1 \neq c_2, p_1 \neq p_2.$

Substituting the values $p_1 = 6, p_2 = 9, c_1 = -32, c_2 = -20$, gives

$$x = \frac{(-32 \times 9) - (-20 \times 6)}{-32 - (-20)} = 14.$$

What a tour around the houses to reach next door. Mair's last question on the rule of double false position is posed in rhyme:

> When first the marriage-not was tied
> Betwixt my wife and me,
> My age did hers as far exceed,
> As three times three does three;
> But after ten and half ten years,
> We man and wife had been,
> Her age came up as near to mine,
> As eight is to sixteen.
> Now, tyro skilled in numbers, say
> What were our ages on our wedding day?

(If you solve this problem, you will discover, with distaste, that the bride was very young. In fact, until 1929 under Scots Law, the legal age of marriage was 14 for boys, 12 for girls, neither party requiring parental consent.)

Extraction of roots

It is strange that in a textbook published almost one hundred and seventy years after Napier's logarithms first saw the light of day, no use is made of them. The readers offered instead standard number-crunching algorithms for the extraction of roots, or *evolution* as it was called.

Example: To find $\sqrt{772.84}$

1. Pair off the digits in both directions from the decimal point. Each pair of digits is called a period and gives a single digit to the root.
2. P, the first digit of the root, is the largest digit such that $p^2 \le 7$, i.e. $p = 2$.
3. Subtract p^2 from 7 to give 3 and bring down the next period to produce the new 'resolvent', 372.
4. Double the answer so far, $2 \times 2 = 4$, to give the first figure of the next divisor. Then find q, the largest digit such that $q(40 + q) \le 372$. Since $7 \times 47 = 329$, $q = 7$.
5. Again subtract and bring down the next period to give 4384.
6. Double the answer so far, $27 \times 2 = 54$, to give the first two digits of the new divisor. Then find r, the largest digit such that $r(540 + r) \le 4384$. Since $8 \times 548 = 4384$, $r = 8$.

$$
\begin{array}{r}
p \quad q \quad r \\
2\overline{)7,72.84} \\
4 \\
\hline
47)372 \\
329 \\
\hline
548)\,4384 \\
4384 \\
\hline
\end{array}
$$

Hence $\sqrt{772.84} = 27.8$.

John Mair explains how the algorithm works:

Now, let the first two periods of the given square number be considered as a square number by themselves; and as every period gives a figure to the root, their root will consist of two figures, or two parts; call the first a and the other y; then $a + y$ is their root complete; and by Euclid ii.4. or by algebraic multiplication, $aa + 2ay + yy$ will be equal to the first two periods of the square number given; and when aa, the square of the first part of the root, is subtracted from the first period, there will remain $2ay + yy$; and to find y, the other part of the root, I divide by its factor or coefficient, viz. by $2a + y$; that is, I find a divisor by doubling the quot, and annexing to it the next quotient-figure.

If there be more periods of the given square number, the two figures now in the quot are to be esteemed the first part of the root; and called a; and by repeating the operation, as above directed, the other part y is found. And if there be still more periods, call the three figures now in the quot a, then repeat the operation, and find y as before. And thus proceed till every period is brought down.

The square root algorithm relies on the utilization of the identity
$$(a + y)^2 \equiv a^2 + y(2a + y).$$
Similarly, cube roots are extracted by expressing $(a + y)^3$ as
$$a^3 + y(3a^2 + 3ay + y^2) \quad *$$
However, the workings become convoluted rather than evoluted!

Example: To find $\sqrt[3]{6.028568}$

	p	q	r
	1.	8	2

$1)\overline{6.028,568}$
$\underline{1}$
$604)5028$
$\underline{4832}$
$98284)\ \overline{196568}$
$\qquad\quad 196568$

Notes:
1. The second digit, q, is the largest digit such that
$$q(3 \times 1^2 \times 100 + 3 \times 1 \times q \times 10 + q^2) \le 5028,$$
10 and 100 being the number base and its square respectively. This expression simplifies to
$$q(300 + 30q + q^2) \le 5028,$$
whence $q = 8$ and $q(300 + 30q + q^2) = 4832$.

2. Likewise, r is found to be 2 from the inequation
$$r(97200 + 540r + r^2) \le 196568$$
as a, in * above, now takes the value 18.

Alligation

Consider the following question:

The owner of a coffee shop blends his own coffee. His standard blend is 3 kg Full French Roast, costing £3.20 per kilogram, with 5 kg Brazilian Santos, costing £3.60 per kilogram. He sells his standard blend at £4.60 per kilogram. Find his profit on the sale of 1 kg of the blend.

173

There are few people in Scotland who blend coffee these days, yet when Mair wrote his book such questions were of great importance to merchants. Indeed, fifteen pages are devoted to the subject of mixing quantities under the heading of 'alligation'. Apparently, alligation may be *medial* or *alternate*, the question above being an example of the former as it requires us to calculate a mean. *Alligation alternate*, the converse of *alligation medial*, deals with questions in which the selling price of the mixture is given and the quantities of each of the ingredients of 'simples' as they are called are to be found. Here is Mair's first example of alligation alternate, along with his rules for the calculation of the answer. (The column labelled 'Differences' has been adjusted to clarify the method.)

> A grocer would mix sugars at 5d, 7d and 10d per lb. so as to sell the mixture or compound at 8d per lb. What quantity of each must he take?

$$
8 \begin{cases} 5 \\ 7 \\ 10 \end{cases}
\begin{array}{l}
\text{Differences} \\
10 - 8 = 2 \\
10 - 8 = 2 \\
8 - 5 = 3 \\
8 - 7 = 1
\end{array}
\quad
\begin{array}{ll}
\text{lb.} & \text{Proof} \\
2 & 2 \times 5 = 10 \\
2 & 2 \times 7 = 14 \\
4 & \underline{2 \times 10 = 40} \\
& 8 \times 8 = 64 \qquad 64
\end{array}
$$

Rules:

I.   Place the rate of the mixture on the left side of a brace as the root: and on the right side of the brace set the rates of the several simples, under one another, as the branches.

II.   Link or alligate the branches, so as one greater and another less than the root may be linked or yoked together. (Note that this can be done in two ways, linking 5 with 10 and 7 with 10, as shown.)

III.   Set the differences betwixt the root and the several branches right against their respective yoke-fellows. These alternate differences are the quantities required.

Problems of this sort can be served up to pupils to help them develop non-algorithmic strategies. It may be necessary to restate them in another form. For example:

> Find weights X kg, Y kg and Z kg which can be hung from the beam balance shown below so that it is in a state of equilibrium.

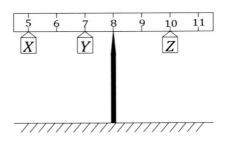

The differences 2, 3 and 1 can be interpreted as the distances, say in units of 10 cm, from the weights to the fulcrum. The simplest integral solution may now be spotted as being $X = Y = 1$ and $Z = 2$ rather than Mair's $X = Y = 2$ and $Z = 4$. Using the same set up but with only two weights so simplifies the problems as to make them suitable for younger or less-able pupils. To stretch the most able, we could extend to four or more weights especially with a view to finding (1) general strategies (2) all integral solutions (3) the condition under which a solution in integers is possible.

6.4 William Playfair's Statistical Diagrams
SMC Journal 51 (2021), pp. 25-35

Introduction

At the dawn of the nineteenth century, a Scotsman published a circular diagram divided into three parts from the unlikely setting of the Fleet, a debtor's prison just north of Ludgate Hill in central London. It purported to represent the land mass of the Turkish Empire, with sectors of appropriate sizes to indicate the fractions of the empire lying in Europe, Asia and Africa, and was rather sloppily coloured by hand. This was the first pie chart and the man was William Playfair.

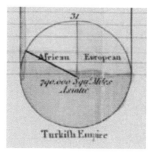

Playfair's innovative pie chart*

Playfair's life: Part 1

Let us begin with William's brother. In 1795, John Playfair (1748–1818) published an edition of Euclid's *Elements* which made use of algebraic notation for the first time and provided a revised version of the troublesome fifth postulate, the form being termed Playfair's Axiom ever since. At the time of the book's publication he had been Professor of Mathematics at the University of Edinburgh for a decade, his earlier career in the ministry set aside. He was a key figure in the Scottish Enlightenment, brushing shoulders with the likes of Adam Smith, Joseph Black, Robert Adam and especially James Hutton, whose uniformitarian theory of geology he promoted.

---

* Figures marked with an asterisk in this section are freely available in the public domain and are republished under a Creative Commons license.

John Playfair was raised in a tiny settlement outside Dundee, the eldest but by no means the only talented member of his family. There were his younger brothers, the lawyer Robert Playfair and the architect James Playfair, as well as James's son, William Henry Playfair, whose architectural legacy is seen in many of the fine buildings in Edinburgh's New Town. And then there was another of John's brothers, William Playfair, engineer, businessman, political economist and scoundrel, but also a visionary when it came to explaining things through diagrams. William, the subject of this chapter, is the father of the statistical diagram and hence a beacon for those who believe that understanding in mathematics and science is often enhanced by the visual.

William Playfair (1759–1823) was taught at home by his father until he was twelve (when his father died) and then by his brother John. He showed an early flair for things mechanical, for draughtsmanship and for model construction, and so it was that he became apprenticed to a local millwright. He was still in his teens when he was introduced to Matthew Boulton, co-owner with James Watt of the Soho Manufactory in Birmingham. They were members of the Lunar Society, and it was through other members of that group, especially James Keir, that they became aware of Playfair's skills as a draughtsman, paving his way to employment. Playfair was soon engaged as Watt's draftsman and clerk, working on improved designs for steam-powered machinery, and then in the on-site assembly and installation of steam-pumping engines.

However, although this work proved a very effective way to further his education, Playfair found the conservatism of the company stifling: there was little 'research and development', as we would call it now. So he left the Soho company and struck out on his own, taking out four patents and starting two companies. He and his brother, James, ran one of these companies from a property much where the BT Tower is now located in London's Fitzrovia. William had taken out a patent to produce cutlery and the like and we know that Josiah Wedgewood bought silverware from Playfair at this time. William and some other business partners also took out a patent for making wooden door and window frames with sashes, and supplied them to the British Museum and to the Prince Regent's Carlton House.

James's architectural business did well and by 1787 he was able to accommodate William and his family in one of the houses he had had built. It was about this time that William met Adam Smith through his elder brother John and this likely triggered his sudden switch of interests towards international business, economics and visual statistics. Prompted by the loss of the American states, he argued that Britain's apparently waning power could be restored by focussing on manufacturing, banking and trade, rather than on the traditional land-grab. His view was that if money were to flow and usury allowed, then investment and speculation would surely follow. His first venture into this new territory saw him drawing time-series charts for a book by Richard Phillips, including graphing six key economic indicators over fifty years to show the effects of the turmoil in both France and America.

The first time-series chart and bar chart

In the early twentieth century, the phrase 'a picture is worth a thousand words', invoked in journalism and advertising, caught the public imagination. In fact, similar ideas had been expressed widely and over a long period of time, including, for example, by Ivan Turgenev who wrote in 1861 that 'the drawing shows me at one glance what might be spread over ten pages in a book'. Back in 1785, William Playfair recognised the possibility not of reducing words to a drawing but of condensing a multitude of numbers into a graph or chart designed to have maximum visual impact on the reader. Essential information could be conveyed more quickly and complex material could be understood by a wider audience. This was a period when Playfair also developed some influential contacts, including Adam Ferguson, recently a cofounder with John Playfair of the Royal Society of Edinburgh, and George Dempster, a scientifically-minded parliamentarian, later put up for fellowship in that body by John Playfair. Dempster wrote gushingly to Ferguson on 8 September 1785 of William Playfair's new statistical graphics. Apparently, *The Commercial and Political Atlas* was to be published in instalments and, by August, Dempster possessed a draft of the first issue (Belhouse, p. 55). The first instalment sold for the very considerable sum of five shillings (a little under £50 in today's money). It contained the first five charts, all time-series charts, of the final book; England's trade with the world, and separately with Ireland, Germany, the West Indies and North America. Upon receiving a copy of this first instalment from Playfair, James Watt told him that the data upon which the charts are constructed should be published with them, otherwise the reader would have to take them on Playfair's authority alone. Playfair decided on a middle path, providing data at intervals of a decade. As part of his research, Playfair's biographer, David Belhouse, analysed the statistics available to Playfair and concluded that he probably smoothed the data, perhaps with the help of a draftsman's spline (made of flexible wood and now termed a 'flexicurve') which were used both at Boulton and Watt for engineering drawings and by James Playfair to produce architectural plans (Belhouse, pp. 59-66).

The full book, 158 quarto pages in landscape orientation, was published in 1786. Such was its success that it was reprinted the following year, with a third edition in 1801 (Playfair, 1786, 1787, 1801b). The last of the three piggy-backed on another major publication of 1801, the *Statistical Breviary* (Playfair, 1801a). From here on in the shortened titles, *Atlas* and *Breviary* will be used.

In the *Atlas*, Playfair's diagram of choice was what we now call the time-series chart; in fact, of the 44 charts the book contains, all but one are time-series charts. As already mentioned, they include the first depictions of a fluctuating balance of trade (i.e. the differences between imports and exports) between England and its trading partners both collectively and individually. But there are also charts showing the national debt since the English Revolution, and changes in the expenditure on the army and navy and on ordnance back to 1720. Importantly, these are not depictions of a functional relationship. The heights of the lines (the value of imports and exports, for example) are not a function of time but a trace of empirical data over time. The figure below shows the very first of those time-series charts in Playfair's book of 1786.

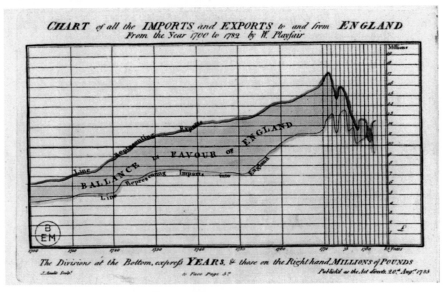

Playfair's first time-series chart*

Notice that all the good features of a statistical graph are in place – title, frame, labelling of the axes, uniform graduation of the scales, grid lines for ease in estimating values and the use of colour to embolden salient features. We wouldn't teach it any differently today. This is how statistical graphs should be drawn and this is how they were drawn from the very first example. Further finessing was never needed because William Playfair had incorporated all the necessary elements from the outset.

This was all very well when it came to picturing England's economic position over time. Playfair had to hand Charles Whitworth's *State of the Trade of Great Britain in Its Imports and Exports*, published in 1776, and the relevant data were included. But when it came to Scotland, Whitworth had included the trade data for just the ten years prior to the Act of Union (1697–1707). Comprehensive data would soon be available from David Macpherson (*Annals of Commerce*, 1805) but Playfair was keen to get into print and so he decided to focus on a single year, and rather than pooling the figures for different countries he chunked the information country by country to produce the first bar chart. In a sense, he had stumbled across the bar chart because his data were incomplete. He commented that 'this chart ... does not comprehend any portion of time, and is much inferior in utility to those that do' (Playfair, 1786, p.101). Today, we would call the diagram a dual bar chart because it compares imports and exports in a pair of horizontal bars, country by country. Note that Playfair also ordered the countries by the volume of trade for ease of comparison. Particularly striking is the volume of imports from Catherine the Great's Russia.

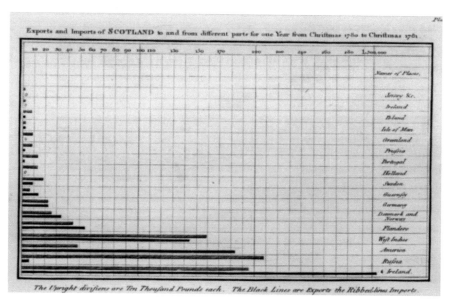

The first (dual) bar chart*

Another book, *Lineal Arithmetic*, appeared in 1798. Privately published, it ran to 72 pages and contained 35 engraved charts depicting the economic performance of England in the eighteenth century. To save money, Playfair resorted to stippling and hatching (the use of dots and strokes), standard techniques in engineering drawing. Among the conclusions that could be drawn from the charts was the likely military capability of a nation and the nature of that capability. Who could put men into the field and who could afford to produce military equipment became clear in a few glances. The book sold poorly and already in debt and with a wife and six children to support, Playfair saw the meagre profits go straight to his creditors.

Playfair's life: Part 2

While the new statistical diagrams would make for ease of understanding, they could also be used to change perceptions and to influence policy, and having dipped his toe in the water with his earlier monograph, Playfair knew this well. The 'Eden Treaty' of 1786 had reduced tariffs between Britain and France, and there was an immediate opportunity for trade to flourish between the countries. So Playfair took himself off to Paris and, through his contacts there, a copy of the *Atlas* was presented to the king, Louis XVI, who, as Playfair later recalled (see Friendly & Wainer, 2021, p. 119),

> 'at once understood the charts and was highly pleased. He said they spoke all languages and were very clear and easily understood.'

Apparently, he was so impressed that when Playfair saw an opportunity to build a rolling mill on an island in the Seine, the king immediately issued a royal patent. And with such royal favour, it is no surprise that when Playfair attended the Académie Royale des Sciences he was warmly welcomed, including by the mathematicians Condorcet, Monge and Vandermonde. By the spring of 1789, his language skills improved to the point he could produce *Tableaux d'Arithmétique Linéaire*, an abbreviated version in French of two books, the *Atlas* and *Essay on the National Debt*. He presented a copy of the new book to the Académie Royale des Sciences and sent a copy to Thomas Jefferson, then the American ambassador in Paris.

When the Bastille was stormed in July 1789, Playfair was living close-by and is known to have attended a meeting to organise a local militia the day before. Although he did not take part, he witnessed much of the action and reported on it in detail later. He stayed in Paris right through the Revolution, all the while becoming more disenchanted with developments. On one occasion in 1791 he bravely intervened when a friend was slashed repeatedly with sabres by a mob intent on killing him.

Among the contemporary observers was the leading French author, François-René Chateaubriand (1768–1848), who commented that, 'some took the road of revolution; others made plans for civil war; others set off for Ohio, sending on ahead plans of country houses to be built among the savages ... all this cheerfully and often without a sou in their pockets' (Chateaubriand, 1961). The reference to the Ohio is relevant to our story. Playfair had been approached by an American agent of a company selling land on the Ohio River to work as an intermediary with potential buyers. He initially declined but, in the period immediately after the Revolution, he argued that the land could be sold in small units to emigrants fleeing France for a safer life. He helped to set up a company to handle the subdivision, but short on financial acumen, and with the French press noisily opposed to the scheme, investors fell away dramatically. In July 1790, the company folded. (Playfair's brother, James, had even designed a plan for a new American city of Gallipolis resembling James Oglethorpe's plan of Savannah, Georgia, but without the public squares.) While about sixty settlers left on the first boat and more followed, there was soon a clamour for repatriation to France. Playfair was made a scapegoat for the failure of the scheme and unjustly accused of embezzlement.

Meanwhile, in Paris, Playfair was running up debts and his creditors were on his tail. By 1792 his concerns about Jacobinism were so great, including the growth of a similar movement back home, that he alerted his countrymen to the dangers in *A Letter to the People of England on the Revolution in France*. Counterfeiting was a serious problem in many countries at the end of the eighteenth century. Up to two-thirds of the coins in circulation in Britain were fake. And so it was that the Bank of England stopped minting copper coins altogether in 1773 leaving a vacuum that was initially taken up by the Parys Mines company on Anglesey which minted tokens directly from its own copper. But it was Boulton and Watt that took on the venture in more earnest, establishing the Soho Mint within the Soho Manufactory in the 1780s. Playfair had left the company by this point but he would have been aware of the problem with the coinage, and the opportunities that the production of token coins and indeed token notes provided, opportunities to turn a profit on a personal level but also to flip an economy given the right circumstances. *A Letter to the People of England* included Playfair's analysis of the weaknesses in France's finances, noting in particular the use of *assignats*, paper money backed by property rather than gold, and printed by the revolutionary government in huge quantities in order to maintain liquidity but at the cost of inflation. Playfair suggested damaging the French economy further by flooding the country with forged assignats, and while the extent of his influence is not clear, it is well documented that French émigrés backed by the British government set up forging operations, with pockets of their activity around Britain, paper production here, engravers there.

An assignat for 400 livres*

Following the execution of Louis XVI in January 1793, the French declared war on Britain and their recent invention, the telegraph, gave them an edge in terms of communications. A series of towers each featuring a mechanical semaphore system were aligned to pass messages quickly. Playfair learnt the details from a member of the Bordeaux parliament and produced a working model. The information was passed up the military chain of command right through to the commander-in-chief, (The Grand Old) Duke of York. Bruce Berkowitz has claimed that Playfair was a spy but most of the details of the telegraph were in the public domain in France and, in short time, in England too. David Belhouse has checked the Royal Archives in Windsor which contain the official records of Britain's spying activity and there is no mention of Playfair for the years 1779 to 1801.

In the late 1790s, Playfair returned to business and specifically to banking, setting up the Original Security Bank and a scheme to print low denomination banknotes ostensibly backed by the Bank of England. But the Bank of England cried foul, and this, combined with considerable mismanagement, led to the bank going bust. Ten months after the venture began, Playfair was bankrupt, and his subsequent failure to attend a meeting called by the bankruptcy commissioners led to his arrest; in the summer of 1798 he spent two months in Newgate prison. A pattern of debt to the point of bankruptcy and the associated imprisonment usually in the Fleet debtors' prison, rather than Newgate, had begun. But being incarcerated rarely stemmed Playfair's output. As Bruce Berkowitz commented (p. 247), 'Playfair was trying to write his way out of debt. The result: some of the most important works in statistics, economics, and strategic analysis were written in London's Fleet Prison'.

The first circle area chart, pie chart and 'annulus chart'

The *Breviary* arose out of a project to marshall and publish descriptive, cartographic and statistical material about a number of European countries. Playfair's starting point was *Statistische Uebersichts-Tabellen aller Europäischen Staaten*, compiled by Jakob Bötticher (1754–1792) in Königsberg in 1790. Playfair translated the book into English, rearranged its contents and changed the units to those used in Britain. As he was released from the Fleet in late 1801, Playfair's *Statistical Breviary* appeared in print. It contained in graphics much of what Bötticher had published in numbers, with coverage extended to India, then an important contributor to the British economy. The book consisted of 64 pages, most of them displaying tables of data, country by country, but with four plates, the most famous of which, 'Statistical chart showing the extent, the population and revenues of the principal nations of Europe in the order of their magnitude' is shown on the next page. It features the first pie chart.

In fact, the chart boasts three innovative features. First, circles are drawn with areas that are proportional to the areas of the countries in square miles, and displayed in descending order. Playfair wrote on page 15 that 'where the forms are not similar, the eye cannot compare them easily nor accurately', effectively arguing that the areas of two or more countries on a map cannot be compared as easily as if those areas are reduced to circles (which are necessarily similar). Different colours are used to indicate whether a country's military power arises from the strength of its navy or its army.

Second, vertical sticks are used to show two quantities: the population in millions represented by a stick to the left of a circle and read using the scale on the left; the budget in millions of pounds sterling represented by a stick to the right of a circle and measured using the right-hand scale. The tops of the sticks for each country are joined with a sloping line. Playfair mistakenly thought that the gradients of these lines give a measure of the burden of taxation on the individual, the steep positive gradient for Britain, for example, highlighting just how heavily the British were taxed. In fact, a comparison of these lines, one country to another, is not possible because each gradient is affected by the radius (and hence the area of the country), so he somewhat fudged the issue.

The third feature, the subdivision of circles into sectors or annuli so that constituent parts can also be considered, requires detailed description and analysis. Subdivision of two of the circles, those for Russia and Turkey, indicate the extent to which they straddle two or more continents. Note here that Playfair uses two different approaches, and this begs the question, 'Why?' For the Russian Empire, its European territories appear as a circle while its Asian territories form an annulus wrapped around it. But for the Turkish (Ottoman) Empire, which encompassed not just modern-day Turkey but Greece, Syria, Iraq and the Caucasus, as well as most of Mediterranean Africa, there is a single circle, proportional in area to the outer circle for Russia, but subdivided into sectors for Europe, Asia and Africa; what we now call a pie chart.

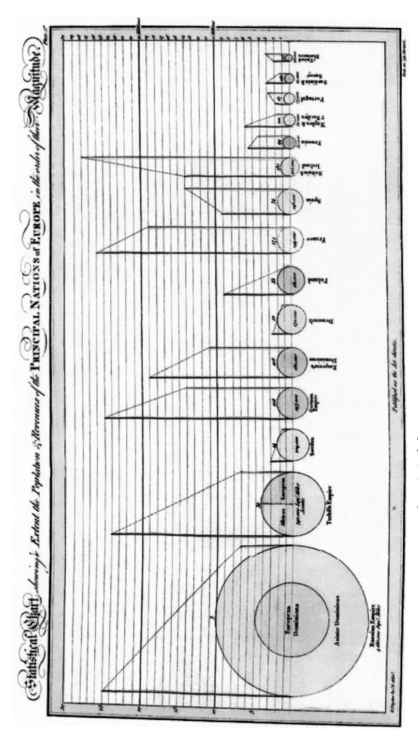

A statistical chart to compare European countries*

As to why Playfair offers two different ways of dividing the circle, one possibility concerns the practicalities of drawing the diagrams. The circles are small, apparently just big enough in the case of Russia that the 'annulus chart' works but too small in the case of the Turkish Empire for three bounding concentric circles to be drawn and the spaces between them coloured. If this theory is correct, then Playfair favoured the concentric circles approach and adopted the radial division method only when it broke down, just as the bar chart emerged from a failure to produce a time-series chart.

The first 48 pages of the book survey the historical picture of fourteen states in detail and allude to another twelve. But in the years since the publication of the *Atlas*, Europe had been in turmoil, the French Revolution itself spilling out into neighbouring countries, the rise of Napoleon and the prosecution of a pan-European war. So while it is possible that it was always Playfair's intention to finish the study at that point, changing circumstances made that impossible. The book was simply brought up-to-date with a further five pages and one plate on the changed state of Europe and an addendum on India (termed 'Hindustan', Persian for the 'lands of the Indus') and more specifically, British India.

A repurposed annulus chart and an early 'Venn diagram'

While Playfair was writing the *Breviary*, Napoleon continued to conduct the Revolutionary Wars (specifically, the War of the Second Coalition) against Austria, Russia, Turkey, Britain and other countries. But the Austrians, defeated at the Battle of Marengo, sued for peace and so whilst the British fought on, under the Treaty of Lunéville in February 1801, French territorial gains were legitimised. This required Playfair to include an updated chart on page 48 towards the end of the main section of the *Breviary*.

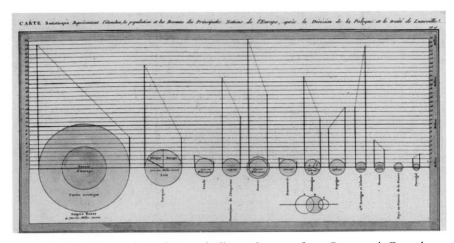

Adjusted chart to show the Lunéville settlement, from Donnant's French version of Playfair's *Breviary* (see below)

The revised diagram has a red annulus around the circle for France to show its territorial gains during the First Republic, supplemented further with some foreign enclaves and new territories – the Austrian Netherlands, the left bank of the Rhine, Savoy and Geneva. This might be thought of as a before-and-after annulus chart or a growth annulus chart; the circle for France used in the *Statistical Breviary* has gained a band rather than an increased radius and subdivision into two sectors. With France's land area now surpassing the areas of Poland and Denmark, its chart is shifted two places to the left.

Meanwhile, a weakened Germany saw its circle slip in the opposite direction and its complex constituent parts marked. Playfair wrote (p. 50):

'... the most interesting situation exhibited is that of the German empire; for in the first place it is diminished in extent; it is in the next place so situated politically that all its internal unanimity is destroyed from the necessary and natural operation of opposite interests.

'That empire may be considered as divided into three parts, Austria, Prussia and Other German Princes, which make three bodies with different, if not rather opposite, interests. To illustrate this, the three circles A, B, and C, are drawn intersecting each other. The circle A represents the German empire as it now is in its full extent. B represents the dominions of the emperor, and C the dominions of Prussia. The red part shows how much of the empire belongs to the house of Austria; the yellow portion represents what belongs to Prussia, and consequently the green, which is all that remains to the other princes, is what may alone truly be called the German empire.'

 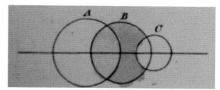

Detail of pie chart and associated 'Venn diagram'

The relevant parts of the chart are depicted in greater detail above. While the three land areas in the pie chart are by necessity disjoint, the interests of the three parts overlap, so that A and B have shared interests, B and C have different shared interests and A and C have no shared interests at all. The intersecting circles figure has been likened to the later Venn diagram and perhaps not unreasonably so because it shows relationships with the matter of scale somewhat suppressed; they are simply representational. Notice that the sloppiness of the shading here supports the hypothesis about the need to abandon annulus charts for subdivision into three or more parts.

The *Breviary* was quickly translated into French by Denis-François Donnant, Secretary of the Société Académique des Sciences. This 1802 volume includes a statistical chart of Hindustan, with no pie chart but another annulus chart and another intersecting circles diagram (shown on the next page).

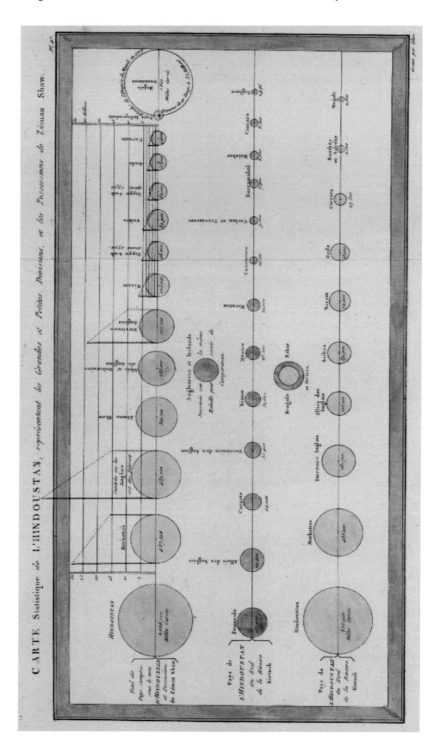

Hindustan chart with Bengal annulus
(David Rumsey Map Collection, Stanford Libraries; Creative Commons License 3.0)

The key detail is the Bengal annulus chart in the lower-central part of the full chart.

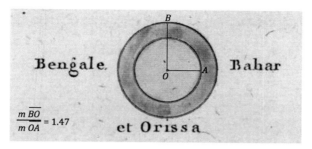

Bengal annulus (dropped into *Geometer's Sketchpad*)

Now the rights to collect revenues in Bengal, Bihar and Odisha had been 'acquired' by Robert Clive in 1765. (Clive was a reviled asset-stripper in his day, his reputation as black at the time as it is in retrospect.) It is not apparent whether the outer circle of Playfair's annulus chart is for Bengal, the inner circle for Bihar and the annulus itself for Odisha, or if the inner circle is for Bengal and Bihar/Odisha the annulus, or if indeed there is some other arrangement, and the political and military manoeuvrings of the time are incredibly complex. But in a sense that doesn't matter because we are focused more on the success or otherwise of Playfair's selection of an annulus chart over a pie chart. If the figure is blown up and dropped into a dynamic geometry package, we find that the ratio of radii is about 1.47 : 1, equating to an area ratio (annulus to circle of about 1.16 : 1). Had Playfair drawn this diagram as a pie chart, the sector angles would have been 193° and 167° and it would have been clear-cut as to which territory had the larger area, something the Bengal annulus chart singularly failed to do.

Donnant had enhanced what Playfair had done by including data relating to the USA, and so Playfair translated Donnant's work back into English as *The Statistical Account of the United States of America* (1805). Its full title finished with 'illustrated by a divided circle … by a new method, engraved and illuminated'. This was Playfair's pie chart, drawn to show the areas of the states in relation to each other and to the country as a whole, and making plain the effect of the Louisiana Purchase from France just two years earlier. The book was dedicated by Playfair to Thomas Jefferson who had just begun his second term as the third American President and he sent him 25 copies.

The pie chart is poorly constructed for, as Belhouse has pointed out, Playfair was shockingly casual in his approach to land measurement (Belhouse, p. 199). For each member of the Union he simply took Donnant's length and width measurements and multiplied them together as if dealing with a perfect rectangle. Furthermore, he inadvertently switched the resulting areas for two states. But he was right to dismiss Donnant's figure for the area of Louisiana (only a sixth of its actual value) and use a much better estimate. And by labelling the sectors, Playfair had completed the process of bringing pie charts into accord with how we would draw them today. The pie chart might not have been fully-fledged in 1801 but it was ready to fly within four years. And if indeed, Playfair initially favoured the annulus chart over the pie chart, then the much greater number of sectors required here certainly settled the issue.

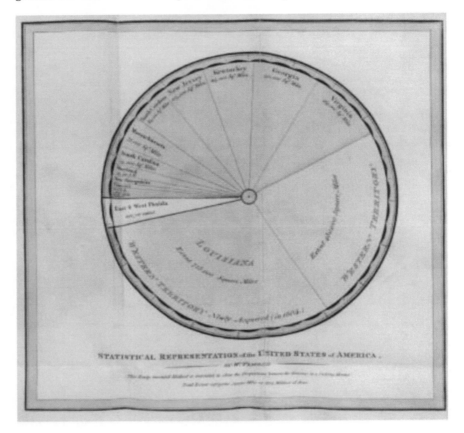

Playfair's American pie chart
(Creative Commons 4.0: Ursinus College)

Eclipsing Adam Smith and anticipating David Ricardo

By 1805 Playfair had a reputation as an original writer on politics and economics. So, with the copyright having run out on Adam Smith's *Wealth of Nations* in 1804, its author long dead, it was Playfair who was entrusted with producing a new edition. This duly appeared in 1805, though Thomas Malthus would comment on the galley proofs that there were serious omissions. Later the same year, Playfair produced *Decline and Fall of Powerful and Wealthy Nations*, with a nod towards Edward Gibbon's analysis of the decline of Rome but with greater generality. The cycle of a nation is little different to a human cycle, he claimed, from birth through growth to greatest strength and health and on in decline towards death. His 'chart of universal commercial history' depicts the fortunes of 21 states over the centuries, each state's period of power being shown as a mountain, its height at any time indicating its approximate power, its length indicating the period of that rise and decline (see Belhouse, p. 208). Its novelty is again of note, though it is designed for politicians and economists rather than statisticians. Playfair also reiterated in this book that the policy of extending a country's territories through conquest should be abandoned in favour of developing its commercial strengths. Jonathan Sachs argued that the book constitutes the 'first attempt at a general and comparative theory of the rise and fall of nations' (Sachs, 2012). It contains the idea of 'comparative advantage', a concept in economics to which David Ricardo's name is attached despite Playfair's priority (see Berkowitz, 2018, p. 268).

The education of women

Decline and Fall also emphasised the need for entrepreneurs, that they would emerge only through education and, since the education of the young was largely in the hands of women, they themselves must be educated to a good standard. Playfair argued that girls should be educated to the age of thirteen or fourteen. A selection of quotes from the *Inquiry* (pp. 99-101) will give a flavour of his views:

> 'When they become wives and mothers, when the economy of the family, and the education of the younger children depend chiefly on them, they are then of very great importance to society. Their conduct in that important situation must be greatly influenced by their education.'

> 'Female education ought then ... to be attended to in the same manner as the education of youth of the other sex.'

> 'There is too much pains taken with adorning the person, and too little with instructing the mind.'

> 'If the women of a nation are badly educated, it must have a great effect on the education of their sons.'

> 'The great general error consists in considering the woman merely in her identical self, without thinking of her influence on others.'

To Playfair, this was economics, not equality of opportunity, though it perhaps had a small role in what was to become a movement later in the nineteenth century.

Playfair's life: Part 3

Playfair found himself on the wrong side of the law in 1805 supporting one of his business partners in hiding monies from creditors during bankruptcy proceedings. When summoned to appear in court, he chose instead to go into hiding for no less than three years. Of his four surviving children, one was blind. There were mouths to feed and no source of income, though a writers' charity did provide ten guineas. In his desperation, in 1808, he turned to extortion, demanded hush money from Spencer Perceval, then Chancellor of the

Exchequer, but by including his address on the letter he was easily tracked down and arrested. In April 1809 he was sentenced to three months in Newgate and he was still in debt. In another scam in 1813 he tried much the same extortion tactic with George Canning but his target didn't take the bait. And he was at it again in 1814, though the scheme was different this time, offering the government information on Napoleon's plan to escape from Elba in exchange for sufficient funds to allow him to travel to the continent. He was in possession of an address to be given by Napoleon to the people of France. It was in code but Playfair also had the key to the code. When Napoleon subsequently escaped, and piqued by being ignored by the government, Playfair went to the press. But the address and the key to its decipherment were phoney, written by Playfair himself in imperfect French. In 1815 he tried again, claiming he could discover important details of a plot in Paris if only the government would finance his passage; again the bait wasn't taken. The following year he attempted to extort money from the engineer, John Rennie, ostensibly protecting this decent man from claims of corruption in public works. He met Rennie and dropped the matter. Also in 1816, he tried to swindle Archibald Douglas by supressing documents questioning his parentage; again the target didn't play ball. And in a rather pathetic attempt to extort money from Viscount Sidmouth he invoked his blind daughter's plight. Collectively, these attempts to weasel money out of others damaged Playfair's reputation.

The graver Playfair's financial circumstances became, the larger the projects he undertook to correct the situation. He embarked on the nine-volume *British Family Antiquity*, subsequently published between 1809 and 1811, cataloguing the aristocracy (to Playfair, the natural ruling class) and their historical lines from the point of their gentrification. While he left the research to others, he did have to raise £5,000, a huge sum, for it to be undertaken but with subscribers signing up, there was the potential of £24,000 of sales, according to Belhouse (p. 220). Families were asked to send details of their forebears and Playfair devised novel ways of displaying the information. One of Playfair's charts is given by Belhouse (p. 225); it is of the English viscounts and barons, a large ordered array of bars differentiated by colour to indicate the source of the original title. But overall the research was slipshod and the volumes on genealogy came in for significant criticism and the publishers, not Playfair himself, were bankrupted by the project.

Playfair's last publication might have been a statistical account of the départements of France. At the beginning of 1820, he had thoughts about such a project but with his health failing and subjected to intermittent spells in prison, the project did not come to fruition. In 1822 Playfair spent several months in the Fleet and by the time he left he had developed a gangrenous leg. He survived only a few weeks into 1823.

There are still two matters to be considered in greater detail:

- How a lad from a tiny community outside Dundee came to produce statistical diagrams. Where did the ideas come from?
- What did Playfair himself consider to be the merits of his diagrams?

Playfair's inspiration

So where did William Playfair's ideas come from and why did he call his approach 'lineal arithmetic'? Some have argued that they came from his employment at Boulton and Watt and certainly there were design features and automated pressure recordings attached to Watt's machines that could have made an impression. But if Playfair's own words are our guide on this matter, then the hand of his elder brother, the mathematician John Playfair, comes into focus, and this takes us back to where we began. The most overt reference is to be found in a footnote on page xvi of the *Inquiry* (1805):

> 'I think it well to embrace this opportunity ... of making some return, (as far as acknowledgement is a return) for an obligation, of a nature never to be repaid, by acknowledging publicly that, to the best and most affectionate of brothers, I owe the invention of those Charts.

> 'At a very early period of my life, my brother, who, in a most exemplary manner, maintained and educated the family his father left, made me keep a register of a thermometer, expressing the variations by lines on a divided scale. He taught me to know that, whatever can be expressed in numbers, may be represented by lines. The Chart of the thermometer was on the same principle with those given here; the application only is different. The brother to whom I owe this, now fills the Natural Philosophy Chair in the University of Edinburgh.'

John Playfair's research in meteorology did indeed generate a huge body of data which was published in the *Transactions of the Royal Society of Edinburgh*. These data were later quoted by Humboldt in his *Isothermal Lines and the Distribution of Heat on the Earth* (1817). So it is not at all surprising that William called his methods 'lineal arithmetic'.

We know that John Playfair was conversant with the writing of Richard Price, a writer on actuarial science, who was also responsible for bringing a 1763 essay of Thomas Bayes to publication. In the main part of the essay Bayes gave us Bayes' Theorem (for finding the probability of a cause from an effect) and Price appended twenty pages of examples (Stigler, 2018). William Playfair met Richard Price at the end of 1786 and discussed a new draft essay of Playfair's on the national debt. Price was impressed by the argument but also commented that Playfair's diagrams were 'agreeable' and 'useful' (Belhouse, p. 66).

John Playfair also knew of David Hartley's *Observations on Man* which alluded to Bayes's thinking prior to the publication of his ideas and he was familiar with Roger Boscovich's work, a precursor to Karl Pearson's on fitting a straight line to data (Stigler, 2018 and 1986). In short, it appears that William's elder brother had some understanding of developments in probability and statistics in the middle of the eighteenth century. William's claim that he was much influenced by his brother therefore seems completely plausible.

The advantages of statistical diagrams

Playfair's statistical diagrams, some 177 of them, were published in three clusters over 36 years (Costigan-Eves and Macdonald-Ross, p.319). From 1786 to 1801, the focus was on time-series charts to display financial information over time; from 1801 to 1805, his attention turned to novel forms, circles and parts of circles; from 1821 onwards, there was a return to line graphs.

The comparisons that Playfair asked his readers to make were comparisons of areas. This is obviously the case with circle charts and pie charts but not so obvious when it comes to time-series charts. But his use of colour or other shading (stippling or hatching) between lines is designed to draw the eye to those regions of the graphs rather than to the lines themselves. It is the shape of the region which impresses on the eye; as we scan from left to right (the passage of time) we can judge whether the region is narrowing or widening.

Playfair proposed a number of advantages of using statistical diagrams. By making use of the research findings of Costigan-Eaves and Macdonald-Ross (1990), these advantages may be distilled into the following four, here listed with examples:

1. Speed of interpretation and attractiveness of learning

    '... no study is less alluring or more dry and tedious than statistics, unless the mind and imagination are set free to work' (*Breviary*, p. 16).

    'Men of great rank, or active business, can only pay attention to general outlines, nor is attention to particulars of use, any farther than they give a general information ... with the assistance of these Charts, such information will be got, without the fatigue and trouble of studying the particulars of which it is composed' (*Atlas*, 1786, p. 4).

2. Ease of interpretation

    'Information, that is imperfectly acquired, is generally as imperfectly retained; and a man who has carefully investigated a printed table, finds, when done, that he has only a very faint and partial idea of what he has read; and that like a figure imprinted on sand, is soon totally erased and defaced. The amount of mercantile transactions in money, and of profit or loss, are capable of being as easily represented in drawing, as any part of space, or as the face of a country; though, till now, it has not been attempted. Upon that principle these Charts were made; and while they give a simple and distinct idea, they are as near perfect accuracy as is any way useful. On inspecting any one of these Charts attentively, a sufficiently distinct impression will, be made, to remain unimpaired for a considerable time, and the idea which does remain will be simple and complete, at once including the duration and amount' (*Atlas*, 1786, pp. 3-4).

    '... tables are by no means a good form for conveying such information ... I can see no kind of advantage in that sort of representation ...' (*Breviary*, Preface).

3. Appeal to the eye

    'As the eye is the best judge of proportion, being able to estimate it with more quickness and accuracy than any other of our organs, it follows, that wherever relative quantities are in question, a gradual increase or decrease of any revenue, receipt or expenditure, of money, or other value, is to be stated, this mode of representing it is peculiarly applicable; it gives a simple, accurate, and permanent idea, by giving form and shape to a number of separate ideas, which are otherwise abstract and unconnected' (*Atlas*, 3rd edition, p. x.).

    '... making an appeal to the eye when proportion and magnitude are concerned, is the best and readiest method of conveying a distinct idea' (*Breviary*, p. 4).

    In the expanded introduction to the third edition of the *Atlas* Playfair explains on p. xi his 'lineal arithmetic' by invoking an imaginary merchant who is paid exclusively in guineas, the standard gold coin until 1816. If he were to stack his guineas for one day, then append stacks on subsequent days until there was a straight line of such stacks shoulder to shoulder, then, he wrote, 'lineal arithmetic ... is nothing more than those piles of guineas represented on paper, and on a small scale, in which an inch (suppose) represents the thickness of five millions of guineas'.

4. Increased efficiency of learning

    'Whatever presents itself quickly and clearly to the mind, sets it to work, to reason and think; whereas, it often happens, that in learning a number of detached facts, the mind is merely passive, and makes no effort further than an attempt to retain such knowledge' (*Breviary*, 1801, p.7).

    'The advantages proposed by this mode of representation, are to facilitate the attainment of information, and aid the memory in retaining it: which two points form the principal business in what we call learning, or the acquisition of knowledge' (*Breviary*, 1801, p.14).

Playfair was also aware of how statistical diagrams could be designed to mislead. In the first edition of the *Atlas* he wrote, 'As to the propriety and justness of representing sums of money, and time, by parts of space, tho' very readily agreed to by most men, yet a few seem to apprehend there may possibly be some deception in it, of which they are not aware ...' (*Atlas*, 1786, iii). Written in this way it is difficult to know whether he is saying that some people have seen his graphs and are wary of their veracity or that he knows how to tweak a scale for example to bring out, even exaggerate, a particular feature.

Remembering William Playfair

After his death, Playfair's rather colourful life was repainted almost uniformly black, starting with the journalist John Goldworth Alger (1836–1907). In numerous publications, including the *Dictionary of National Biography*, Alger dismissed Playfair as a complete rogue and, critically for our story, made no mention of statistical diagrams. However, an exception can be found at the end of the nineteenth century. Francis Edgeworth, like Playfair an economist with a significant statistical bent, was complimentary about his 'acumen as an economist as well as some originality as a statistician' (Edgeworth, 1899; quoted in Belhouse, p. 277). The next complimentary comment would wait until 1983 when Edward Tufte propelled Playfair's status upwards. His modern biographers, Bruce Berkowitz and David Belhouse, with clear distance between them on some matters, are largely in step on the importance of Playfair's contribution to statistical and economic graphics and on his financial incompetence. Berkowitz notes that there is no image of William Playfair, either in portrait or statue, that he lived a most interesting life never far from penury, and that it was that financial insecurity that drove him forward. And Belhouse (p. 7) comments that 'the flaw that constrained his genius was his continued inability to deal with his personal and professional finances. He was financially inept. Almost always short of money, he spent his life clawing away, trying to keep the wolves from the door ... [and in] his desperation to make ends meet, he often resorted to highly questionable actions ...'

References

Adelman, J. 'The man with a finger in many pie charts', *Irish Times* (5 March 2018, online); accessed 18/02/21.

Belhouse, D. R. *The Flawed Genius of William Playfair: The Story of the Father of Statistical Graphics*, University of Toronto Press, 2023.

Berkowitz, B. D. *Playfair: The True Story of the British Secret Agent Who Changed How We See the World*, George Mason University Press, Fairfax VA, 2018.

Chateaubriand, F-R. *The Memoirs of Chateaubriand*, translated and edited by Robert Baldick, London: Hamish Hamilton, 1961; also in the Penguin Classics series (1965).

Costigan-Eves, P. and Macdonald-Ross, M. 'William Playfair, (1759–1823)', *Statistical Science* 5, 3 (1990), pp. 318-326.

Friendly, M. 'A brief history of data visualization', in Chen, C., Härdle, W. & Unwin, A. (eds.), *Handbook of Computational Statistics: Data Visualization III*, Springer-Verlag, 2008.

Friendly, M. & Wainer, H. *A History of Data Visualization and Graphic Communication*, Harvard University Press, 2021.

Playfair, J. G. (ed.) *The Works of John Playfair*, Edinburgh: Constable, 1822.

Playfair, W. *The Commercial and Political Atlas*, London: Debrett; Robinson, and Sewell, 1786.

Playfair, W. *The Commercial, Political and Parliamentary Atlas*, London: Stockdale, 1787.

Playfair, W. *Lineal Arithmetic*, London: private publication printed by Alexander Paris, 1798.

Playfair, W. *The Statistical Breviary, Shewing on a Principle Entirely New, The Resources of Every State and Kingdom in Europe, Illustrated with Stained*

Copper-Plate Charts, Representing the Physical Powers of Each Distinct Nation with Ease and Perspicuity, London: T. Bentley, 1801a. A digitised version of a copy held in the Bodleian Library, University of Oxford, is at: https://archive.org/details/statisticalbrev00playgoog

Playfair, W. *The Commercial and Political Atlas*, 3rd edition, London: J. Wallis, 1801b.

Playfair, W. *An Inquiry into the Decline and Fall of Powerful and Wealthy Nations*, London: Greenland & Norris, 1805. There is an online copy at www.google.co.uk/books/edition/An_Inquiry_Into_the_Permanent_Causes_of/uMVAAQAAMAAJ?hl=en&gbpv=1&printsec=frontcover This is useful for the text, though the charts have been digitised whilst folded and hence remain partially hidden.

Playfair, W. *Outlines of a Plan for a New and Solid Balance of Power in Europe*, London: Stockdale, 1813.

Sachs, J. '1786/1801: William Playfair, Statistical Graphics, and the Meaning of an Event', *BRANCH: Britain, Representation and Nineteenth-Century History*. Ed. Dino Franco Felluga, 2012. Extension of *Romanticism and Victorianism on the Net*; available online at https://branchcollective.org/?ps_articles=jonathan-sachs-17861801-william-playfair-statistical-graphics-and-the-meaning-of-an-event (accessed 28 February2024).

Spence, I. 'William Playfair and the psychology of graphs', *Proceedings of the American Statistical Association, Section on Statistical Graphics* (August 2006), pp. 2426-2436.

Spence, I. & Wainer, H. 'William Playfair and his graphical inventions: an excerpt from the introduction to the republication of his *Atlas* and *Statistical Breviary*', *The American Statistician* 59, 3 (August 2005), pp. 224-229.

Tufte, E. *The Visual Display of Quantitative Information*, Cheshire CT: Graphics Press, 1983 (second edition, 2001).

6.5 Peter Guthrie Tait on the Flight of a Golf Ball

[With the kind permission of The Mathematical Association, this section is taken from 'The golf ball aerodynamics of Peter Guthrie Tait' by Chris Denley and Chris Pritchard' *Mathematical Gazette* Vol. 77, No. 480 (November 1993), pp. 298-313. The analysis of the aerodynamics was undertaken by Chris Denley at BAE Systems, Brough, while my focus was on the historical aspects.]

The anecdote

The eminent Edinburgh physicist, Peter Guthrie Tait, having constructed mathematical models of the flight of a golf ball and having carried out an extensive series of experiments to evaluate their parameters, specified the maximum distance a golf ball could be made to carry by the most accomplished golfer. He was then upstaged by his son who hit a monumental drive which pitched even further. The golfing press of the day – what there was of it – was happy to run the story and scientists themselves seemed to enjoy the joke at

Tait's expense. Macfarlane (1919, p. 52), for example, related the anecdote in the following terms in a lecture delivered just eight months after Tait's death:

> 'He [...] communicated his results to the Royal Society of Edinburgh and there stated definitely the longest distance to which a golf ball could possibly be driven [...] but the champion golfer upset his father's calculations [...] by driving a ball five yards further.'

The upstaging, so the story goes, took place on 11 January 1893. Freddie Tait, the physicist's son, was celebrating his 23rd birthday. The barometer was high at 1045 millibars, the ground was frozen, the air still: a beautiful crisp day at St Andrews, the home of golf. Freddie's brother and his playing partner were on the fairway about to take their second shots to the Hole o' Cross when a 27 Tom Morris sailed right over them and came to rest 341 yards and 9 inches from the tee. Nobody saw just where Freddie's drive pitched and the ball was temporarily lost. Nevertheless, among the "facts incontrovertibly established" and reported in the journal *Golf* on 27 January was that it "carried a minimum distance of 245 yards, and in all probability 5 to 10 yards further than that, on to a table six feet three inches above the level of the teeing ground." Not only is the anecdote an inaccurate account of what took place but it tends to deflect attention from the serious scientific study of the flight of a golf ball which Tait initiated.

Golfing father and son

Peter Guthrie Tait, a native of Dalkeith, succeeded Forbes as Professor of Natural Philosophy, i.e. Physics, at the University of Edinburgh in 1860 and held the post with distinction for forty years. His counterpart at Glasgow University during this period was William Thomson, later Lord Kelvin. The fruit of their collaboration, *Treatise on Natural Philosophy*, became the accepted classic in its field and reestablished the reputation of Newton. Of the mass of scientific material Tait produced – he wrote a paper every 44 days on average – no fewer than thirteen were devoted to the paths of spherical projectiles, especially golf balls and one to the application of probability to the outcome of golf matches.

Tait undoubtedly had a passion for golf. He was a well-known figure at St Andrews from 1868 to the end of his days. In the early years he would play as many as five rounds in a day, beginning at 6.30 a.m., but understandably the number of rounds decreased gradually until by the time he was sixty he was happy to play just the outward nine holes. He possessed a keen sense of fun. Typically, one dark evening Tait coaxed a small group of friends, which included Thomas Huxley and Crum Brown, to play a round of golf with phosphorescent balls. It proved a huge success until Crum Brown's glove burst into flames, burning his hand!

Freddie Tait: as winner of the 1896 (Amateur) Champions Cup (*50 Years of Golf* by Horace Hutchinson, CC0 License) and in the uniform of the Black Watch

Freddie, Peter Guthrie's son, was the leading Scottish amateur golfer of the last decade of the nineteenth century. He was rather wild and unpredictable off the tee but capable of breathtaking recovery shots and brilliance on and around the greens. Despite an early success in reducing the course record at St. Andrews to 72 he had an intense aversion to strokeplay, which he disparagingly likened to rifle-shooting. It was in match play that Freddie was at his most formidable. He reached the final of the British Amateur Championships three times in four years, winning impressively in 1896 and 1898 but squandering a five-hole advantage to lose at the 37th in 1899. Sadly, it was to be a golfing career cut short by war and untimely death. Freddie Tait, a lieutenant in the Black Watch, left for the Boer War in October 1899 and perished at Koodoosberg just three and a half months later on 7 February 1900. His name can be found on the left-hand side of the Boer War memorial plaque on the Mound in Edinburgh.

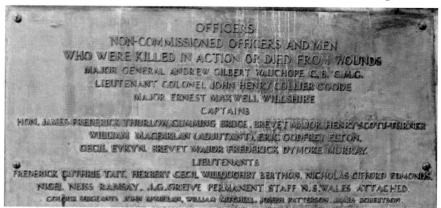

Peter Guthrie had followed his son's progress with pride and in his later years he delighted in the title of 'The father of Freddie Tait'. Freddie and other promising young golfers had reciprocated by helping the scientist with his enquiries into golf ball aerodynamics, hitting balls onto a pad of clay in his laboratory to establish a realistic estimate of the initial velocity. Freddie's death left Peter Guthrie a broken man. His scientific work dried up as his health waned rapidly, but determined to see out the nineteenth century he struggled on at the university until December 1900. Poignantly, in the six months that yet remained of his life, he read and reread J.L. Low's *Record* of the life and golfing achievements of his son.

The deviation of a projectile from a parabolic path: some history

In a letter of 1671 to Henry Oldenburg on the subject of the dispersion of light, Isaac Newton observed indirectly that differences in air pressure cause balls to have a more complex trajectory than a simple parabolic curve. He wrote:

> "I began to suspect that the rays, in their trajection through the prism, did not move in curve lines, and according to their more or less curvity, tend to divers parts of the wall. And it increased my suspicion, when I remembered that I had often seen a tennis ball struck with an oblique racket describe such a curve line. For, a circular as well as a progressive motion being communicated to it by that stroke, its parts, on that side where the motions conspire, must press and beat the contiguous air more violently than on the other; and there excite a reluctancy and reaction of the air proportionately greater."

Benjamin Robins, a Quaker of decidedly non-pacifist interests, transformed the history of external ballistics in a series of experiments in the early 1740s. Using muskets with curved barrels he observed that the musket-ball swerved in the opposite direction to the curvature of the barrel and correctly attributed this deviation to spin. However, despite conducting an ingenious follow-up experiment with a pendulum formed by a sphere rotating on a twisted string he was unable to make predictions for the want of accurately determined coefficients. He had effectively demonstrated the Magnus effect experienced by a sphere a century before Heinrich Magnus did so for cylindrical bodies.

When Robins published his book, *The New Principles of Gunnery*, Leonhard Euler immediately recognised its importance, translating it into German in 1745 and enlarging it in the process. But with his perspicacity for once deserting him, he rejected the rotation hypothesis, arguing instead that any deviation from the ball's natural course "arises from the figure of the ball only". With the matter clearly not settled to everyone's satisfaction the Berlin Academy offered a prize in 1794 for the explanation of the phenomenon but no satisfactory explanation appeared for over half a century. Meanwhile, in 1839, Siméon-Denis Poisson who was also sceptical of the conclusion drawn by Robins, studied the effect of atmospheric friction against the rotating sphere, but finally acknowledged that friction was not sufficient to explain the deviations. (He did correctly attribute the slight bending to the right of projectiles in the northern hemisphere to the rotation of the Earth.)

In a paper presented to the Berlin Academy in 1852, Magnus gave the results of his experiments of the eponymous effect experienced by a cylinder in a wind tunnel. He appeared unaware of the work of Robins even though Euler had held a chair at the Berlin Academy during his years of interest in ballistics. A mathematical explanation was offered by Lord Rayleigh in a paper of 1877 on 'The Irregular Flight of a Tennis Ball'. He averred that there is a difference in pressure at the 'front' and 'back' of the ball in flight, that the force on the ball resulting from such a difference in pressure is perpendicular to its motion and to the axis of rotation, and further, that its magnitude is proportional to the product of the ball's forward and rotational velocities and the sine of the angle between its direction of motion and its axis of rotation.

Meanwhile, Francis Bashforth, Rector of the Parish of Minting near Horncastle from 1857 to 1908 and simultaneously Professor of Applied Mathematics at Woolwich, had designed and built a new chronograph to determine the coefficients of air resistance of ballistics. Between 1865 and 1880 he carried out a plethora of experiments on both spherical ballistics and ballistics with elongated heads of various shapes. By 1881 he had made available tables of coefficients of air resistance for velocities between 100 ft s^{-1} and 2800 ft s^{-1}, tables reproduced by Friedrich Krupp without acknowledgement. Such was the position when Tait's recreational interest in golf spilt over into his scientific life.

Tait's early papers on the physics of golf (1887-91)

In 'The unwritten chapter on golf', an article which appeared in *The Scotsman* newspaper on August 31, 1887 and reproduced in *Nature* the following month, Tait concluded that spin induces a golf ball to deviate from its still-air trajectory and noted that the first section of the path of a ball with back-spin can be concave upwards despite the effect of gravity. Despite this understanding, he began to explore the mathematics of the simpler no-spin trajectory. Indeed, by July 1890, he was reporting to the Royal Society of Edinburgh how he had modelled the trajectory of a golf ball using an equation from a book which he and William Steele had written together in 1856, *Dynamics of a Particle*, viz.

$$y = \left(\tan \alpha + \frac{ga}{2V_0^2} \right) x - \frac{ga^2}{4V_0^2} \left(e^{\frac{2x}{a}} - 1 \right)$$

where α is the initial inclination in degrees, g is the acceleration due to gravity, a is the fixed ratio (in feet) of the square of the velocity to the deceleration caused by air-resistance, and V_0 the initial velocity in feet per second. From experiment and experience he tentatively suggested the following estimates for these parameters: $\alpha = 13.5$, $a = 280$, and $V_0 = 500$. Whence, with $g = 32.174$ ft s^{-2},

$$y = 0.258x - 2.524 \left(e^{\frac{x}{140}} - 1 \right).$$

This trajectory attains a maximum height of 62 ft, 372 ft from the tee, and has a range of 571 ft. Varying the initial velocity gives the following ranges of carry, which were given by Tait in 'Some points in the physics of golf', *Nature*, 1890.

Initial velocity (ft s^{-1})	100	200	300	400	500	600
Range (ft)	112	277	400	497	571	631

For ease of comparison with the spin trajectories shown on pages 199 and 200 we show here Tait's no-spin trajectory with parameters $\alpha = 13.75, a = 360$ and $V_0 = 24$.

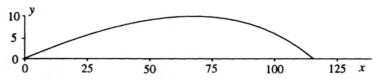

Tait's no-spin trajectory, with axes graduated in metres

In 'Some points in the physics of golf II', published in *Nature* in September 1891, Tait again stressed the importance of imparting back-spin to maximise carry, hence the need to employ a tee which enabled the lower part of the ball to be struck. 'Hammering', which could be carried out with "a few touches skilfully applied with a rough file" allowed the undercut ball to take as much angular velocity as possible, so Tait believed. Eventually he recognised that the roughened ball did not incur increased air-resistance, but he was unable to explain the uneven surface's drag-reducing effect now attributed to turbulence and did not live to witness the advent of the dimpled ball.

Major papers "On the path of a rotating spherical projectile"

Tait wrote two major papers on golf ball paths. The first, entitled 'On the path of a rotating spherical projectile I, entered Vol. 37 of the Transactions of the Royal Society of Edinburgh under the dates June 5 and July 3, 1893. The second, differing in title from the first by the suffix II, appears under the dates January 6 and 20, 1896 in Vol. 39 of the same publication, though, with Tait aiming to furnish more accurate estimates of the model's parameters through experimentation, its appearance in print was delayed until October 5, 1898.

Tait's 1890 model, having ignored the effect of back-spin (or underspin as he called it), consequently lacked power. In fact, with the best golfers driving the ball through the air for six, if not seven, seconds before pitching the model was simply invalid. Moreover, since the article of September 1891 had appeared in *Nature* there had been an outcry from golfers who considered as an affront any suggestion that they imparted spin to the ball to gain extra distance. A complete model, taking the effect of spin into consideration, was clearly needed.

Tait's trajectory

If Tait was initially persuaded to study the aerodynamics of golf balls in order to predict a farthest possible drive then he certainly suppressed this objective, perhaps because it soon became clear that in theory no limiting range appeared to exist, except through human limitations. Instead, he fixed the range at 180 yards or even 165 yards and the duration of flight at about 6 seconds and looked at the effect on the other unknowns: first the coefficient of resistance, then the point of inflection (i.e. where the path ceases to be concave upwards), then the range if no spin is imparted, and finally the location of the vertex if no spin is imparted. The figure below is taken from the last page of Tait's 1893 paper.

Typical Tait trajectories exhibiting upward concavity, range fixed at 165 yards.

He concentrated on validating and refining his model using all the information at his disposal including that from Robins, Magnus and Bashforth, and from personal observation. Diagrammatic interpretations of these situations were offered at the end of each paper. Tait's preferred refinement of the model gives the equation of the trajectory as

$$y = \alpha x + \frac{ka^2}{V_0}\left(e^{\frac{x}{a}} - 1 - \frac{x}{a}\right)x - \frac{ga^2}{4V_0^2}\left(e^{\frac{2x}{a}} - 1 - \frac{2x}{a}\right)$$

where k is a constant of proportionality between lateral acceleration and velocity. It would be appropriate to verify this model using some of the more modern techniques of aerodynamics and computing. However, this kind of endeavour is restricted as certain assumptions still need to be made regarding drag and the equatorial speed of rotation of the ball, w, as Tait himself found.

Tait's assumptions on drag and lift

If the power of a mathematical model lies in its ability to make predictions about the real world, and if its form is determined by the assumptions which underpin it, then the validity of the assumptions is of paramount importance. Sir George Stokes, the Lucasian Professor at Cambridge University, was universally acknowledged to be the leading fluid dynamicist of the time and so it is not at all surprising that Tait turned to him on many an occasion to check whether his assumptions were sensible. It is difficult to gain an appreciation of Tait's work without a critical analysis of those assumptions.

Tait assumed that D, the drag or resistance force, on a ball varies nearly as the square of the speed, founding this belief on the empirical results of his forerunners. The assumption was supported by Stokes in his correspondence with Tait, and is indeed a reasonable one provided that (a) the speed is neither very low nor very high, and (b) air density can be taken to be constant at low speeds. Tait knew of the deviation from this relationship at sonic speed and above. In fact the speed must remain much lower than sonic speed for the relationship to broadly reflect reality. A dimensional analysis will lend some credence to the assumption. If drag, D, be assumed to be a function of velocity, v, density, ρ, and projected frontal area, S, (πr^2 for a sphere), it is not difficult to establish that $D \propto \rho v^2 S$. Hence if ρ and S are constant, $D \propto v^2$.

For convenience the aerodynamicist uses a non-dimensional drag coefficient C_D, defined thus:

$$C_D = \frac{D}{\frac{1}{2}\rho v^2 S}.$$

($\frac{1}{2}\rho v^2$ is the 'kinetic pressure' of Bernoulli's Equation). Hence if $D \propto \rho v^2 S$ then C_D is constant. In reality C_D varies, but can under some circumstances be almost constant, and, as will be seen, we shall have to assume that C_D is constant in much of this study. From his second paper it is apparent that Tait was aware of a likely deviation from the rule that resistance varies as v^2 for low speeds but through lack of information was unable to test this. Lift, L, is defined as a force normal to the direction of motion. Tait referred to lift as a "deflecting force or force perpendicular to both the flight direction and the axis of rotation." In a similar way to the drag coefficient, a lift coefficient is defined in aerodynamics by

$$C_L = \frac{L}{\frac{1}{2}\rho v^2 S}.$$

Lift is generated in the following way. Consider a clockwise rotating ball with its axis fixed in space in an air stream flowing from left to right. The spin causes the air above the ball to accelerate and that below to decelerate. Bernoulli's Equation, (omitting gravitational terms):

$$static\ pressure + \tfrac{1}{2}\rho v^2 = constant\ along\ a\ streamline$$

yields the fact that accelerated flows lead to a drop in static pressure, with deceleration causing an increase. Thus the pressure below the ball is higher than that above and lift is created. Tait quoted Newton's explanation of this pressure difference and went on to make the assumption, supported by Stokes, that L is proportional to vw. Since he had assumed drag to be proportional to the square of the velocity and to be the result of pressure, then the pressures responsible for lift should also be proportional to the square of the velocity. Now the speeds over the ground of the surface of the ball at the very top and the very bottom are $v - w$ and $v + w$ respectively. Thus it can be assumed, crudely, that $L \propto (v + w)^2 - (v - w)^2$. Tait assumed that $L \propto (v + ew)^2 - (v - ew)^2$ but did not clearly explain the incorporation of the constant e. We get L proportional to vw whether or not e is present. Whatever Tait's reasoning, L proportional to vw is a very fair modelling assumption in any case. Since lift must increase with v and w independently, and as Tait noted if either is zero then no lift results, then it reasonable to assume that lift is approximately proportional to both v and w

and thus to their product. Furthermore, this result is analogous to those for the spinning cylinder given by Lord Rayleigh and also by ideal-flow theory.

Tait for the most part assumed w to be constant – a view again supported by Stokes who believed w to be small compared with v and the diminution of w not worth considering. In this study some doubt is cast on the relatively small magnitude of w. Later, Tait considered w as having exponential decay but does not pursue the idea beyond an initial trajectory model, due to lack of experimental information on w and insignificant resulting improvement on his previous (w constant) model.

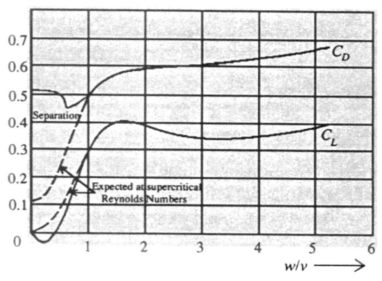

Simplification of Hoerner's "lift and drag characteristics of a sphere"

The $L \propto vw$ assumption can be compared with Horner's modern-day empirical model (Hoerner, 1965). In considering the 'Lift and drag characteristics of a sphere spinning about the horizontal cross-wind axis', Hoerner gives lift data which allow a more accurate estimate of w to be made. It is empirically confirmed that air density remains approximately constant with varying speed, provided that speed is well below that of sound; and with the frontal area of the ball being necessarily constant it follows directly that if $L \propto vw$ then $C_L \propto w/v$. In the figure above, Hoerner gives C_L as a function of w/v and, as can be seen, provided w/v is less than about 1.5, C_L increases with w/v (except very near the origin) and so the linear assumption of Tait again appears a reasonable approximation. It only remains to ascertain a value for (or at least an order of magnitude of) w.

Tait's preferred model

In order to test Tait's trajectory it is necessary to set various parameters. Tait had what might be deemed a preferred typical trajectory with $V_0 = 240$ ft s^{-1}, $a = 360$ ft and range = 180 yd. His estimates of initial inclination were between 13.5° and 14°. Taking say $\alpha = 13.75°$ (0.24 radians) yields $k = 0.151$ s^{-1}, a value notably lower than Tait's original estimate of 0.357 s^{-1}, but certainly of the same order. Note that k is proportional to w and is thus constant only if w is constant, which will be assumed. We now have a simple trajectory near to that favoured by Tait in his 1896 paper

$$y = 0.24x + 81.54\left(e^{\frac{x}{360}} - 1 - \frac{x}{360}\right) - 18.1\left(e^{\frac{x}{180}} - 1 - \frac{x}{180}\right).$$

The maximum height is close to 20 m. Although Tait observed upward concavity in the early stages of a good drive, our trajectory exhibits this effect only in the first fifth of a second or so of the flight. However, with higher values of k, and hence w, upward concavity is more pronouncedly achieved both with Tait's model and with the computer simulation. It is this upward concavity which is the visible effect of lift on a spinning ball. By comparison, Hoerner concludes that for comparatively heavy balls such as those used in golf or baseball "any aerodynamic lift that might develop can have only little effect upon their flight through the air". While Tait's scientific study of this subject was founded on his love of the game and constructed around his extensive personal experience, observation and experiment, Hoerner, it seems, has spent little time watching the great baseball players.

Appraisal of Tait's model using Tait's original assumptions

One way of appraising Tait's model is by making *ab initio* analyses of the trajectory of a spinning golf ball using his assumptions and then comparing the results of our analyses with his model. Using numerical calculus, the time of travel of the ball is split into small elements δt and a recurrence procedure used as the basis of the main loop of the computer algorithm as follows: For the duration of the time interval δt, the forces on, and hence the acceleration of, the ball are assumed constant and then recalculated for the next time interval, along with new values for the forces, the velocity and the angle of inclination.

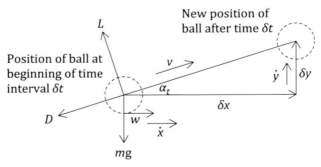

Forces acting on the golf ball in flight

Vertically, we have $\ddot{y} = \dfrac{L\cos\alpha_t - D\sin\alpha_t}{m} - g$,

with $\delta y = \dot{y}\delta t + \dfrac{1}{2}\ddot{y}(\delta t)^2$ and $\dot{y}_{\text{new}} = \dot{y}_{\text{old}} + \ddot{y}\delta t$.

Horizontally, we have $\ddot{x} = \dfrac{-(L\sin\alpha_t + D\cos\alpha_t)}{m}$,

with $\delta x = \dot{x}\delta t + \dfrac{1}{2}\ddot{x}(\delta t)^2$ and $\dot{x}_{\text{new}} = \dot{x}_{\text{old}} + \ddot{x}\delta t$.

Initially, $\dot{x} = V_0\cos\alpha$ and $\dot{y} = V_0\sin\alpha$;

thereafter, $v_{\text{new}} = \sqrt{(\dot{x}_{\text{new}})^2 + (\dot{y}_{\text{new}})^2}$ and $\alpha_{t_{\text{new}}} = \tan^{-1}\left(\dfrac{\dot{y}_{\text{new}}}{\dot{x}_{\text{new}}}\right)$.

Here V_0 and α are the initial velocity and inclination whereas v and α_t are the velocity and inclination at time t. The frontal area is $S = 0.00143$ m^2 and the mass $m = 0.04593$ kg. Air density ρ is taken as 1.225 kg m^{-3} (International Standard Atmosphere, sea level). Results are sensitive to δt until it is reduced to about 0.02 s: consequently $t = 0.01$ s, used here errs on the side of safety. The assumptions made are that C_D is constant (i.e. $D \propto v^2$), w is constant and $C_L \propto w/v$. Trial-and-improvement computer runs, made to get the same range and height as Tait's model, reassuringly rendered lift and drag coefficients of $7.75/v$ and 0.434 respectively as against $7.93/v$ and 0.478 derived from Tait's data. Note that metres per second are used for v here. Now to gain a rough idea of the order of magnitude of w, a straight line through the origin approximation to Hoerner's C_L function, for w/v between 0 and 2 say, suggests that w is roughly 30 ms^{-1} for $C_L = 7.75/v$. The trajectory obtained with $C_L = 7.75/v$ and $C_D = 0.434$ is virtually identical to Tait's trajectory. Time of flight on the computer model is 5.2 s whereas Tait suggests at least 6 s.

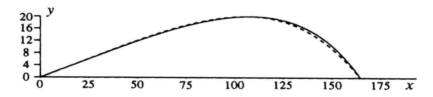

Comparing Tait's preferred trajectory (full line) and the computer trajectory

Using Hoerner's model to appraise Tait's model

Here again the assumptions have to be made that both w and C_D are constant. For the most part, C_D is in the separation region[1] and therefore nothing is known of its variation with w/v. However, Hoerner's lift model is more informative. If an assumed value of w is taken, then measurements from Hoerner's model make

---

[1] Separation is the effect of low-energy flow failing to overcome friction and follow the contours of a body, thus breaking away. According to Hoerner's model, varying the separation has no effect on C_D for $w/v > 1$.

it possible to plot C_L against v. The function $C_L = f(v)$ obtained is used in computer runs to yield C_D consistent with a range of 165 m (180 yd). The exercise is repeated, with adjustments made to w each time, until the maximum height eventually approaches coincidence with Tait's value. With $w = 35$ ms^{-1}, $C_L = f(v)$ approximates the piecewise linear function:

$$f(v) = \begin{cases} 0.495 - 0.00467v & v \le 30 \\ 0.620 - 0.00905v & 30 < v \le 50 \\ 0.385 - 0.0043v & v > 50. \end{cases}$$

The corresponding C_D is 0.464. The trajectory when plotted differs nowhere by as much as 6% from Tait's model. Further refinement of w, an unjustifiably lengthy process, would almost certainly give virtual replication. Instead, a more sensible approach to further study would be to model w as a variable.

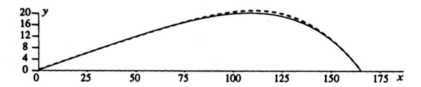

Comparison of Tait's preferred trajectory (full line) and the computer trajectory based on Hoerner's lift model (broken line)

In appreciation

Using Tait's preferred initial velocity and range, Tait's model based on the assumptions that w and C_D are constant and $L \propto vw$ gives a virtually identical trajectory to the computer simulation using the same initial assumptions. The value of C_D in the simulation turns out to be very close to that used by Tait as does the relationship between C_L and v. The use of Hoerner's model to derive C_L (again assuming w constant) makes no appreciable difference to the trajectory, but confirms the order of magnitude of C_D and also that Tait's assumption on lift is a reasonable one in the region under consideration. Hoerner's model also suggests that the magnitude of w is of the order of 30 or 35 ms^{-1}, a size not dissimilar to that of v for the last three-quarters or so of the flight and thus comparable with but in the opposite sense to the spin of a rolling ball, and at odds with Stokes's view that w is substantially less than v. In sum, Tait's attempt to model the flight of a golf ball is a very impressive piece of work. The calculations required to run it and to validate it must have been desperately lengthy and tedious, and though he was ably assisted in this respect by his laboratory student, James Wood, this is still far removed from having access to a modern computer. Tait's development of the trajectory from a gravity-free environment, with lift and drag only, to a realistic vertical plane model with gravitational effects, validated as extensively as existing information and personal observation would allow, shows him to have been a noteworthy mathematical modeller.

The anecdote debunked

Long carrying was just one aspect of the scientific researches which Tait undertook to improve his understanding of aerodynamics. It was an aspect which he played down in his 1893 model by fixing the range in order to discover more about the other parameters. It is true that he was keen to explain to golfers the effect of backspin on range and consequently this became more of a feature in his popular articles on golf. In short, there is a pronounced difference in the amount of stress he gave to long carrying in his scientific and his recreational writings. Freddie's famous drive is more likely to have attained its great distance by running over the hard winter ground after an above-average pitch than by carrying a phenomenal distance. Experiments have shown that a golf ball driven down an airport runway can travel all of 632 yards before coming to rest: an extreme example perhaps of what happens when the surface is very hard. Yet, even today the substantiated records for long carrying are less than half this distance at around the 300-310 yard mark. (Heating golf balls thoroughly to 51° C enables them to travel 8% further.) There are two pieces of evidence which lend weight to this view. First, on the day in question there were adverse climatic conditions for long carrying, a dry cold day with the barometer high. From the Perfect Gas Law, which may be written

$$\frac{P}{T} = \rho R,$$

where P = pressure, T = absolute temperature and R = gas constant, it can be seen that density increases with increase of pressure and decrease of temperature. Furthermore, since $D = C_D(\frac{1}{2}\rho v^2 S)$, drag rises with increased density. Fourteen months before Freddie had made his drive his father had concluded 'Some points in the physics of golf II' with precisely this observation. The coefficient of resistance "has its greatest value, and the drive is accordingly shortest, on a dry cold day with an exceptionally high barometer". The longest drive will of course be when the air is as warm and moist as possible and the barometer very low. Second, nobody witnessed the ball's alighting. Just where it pitched was a matter of conjecture on the part of the golfers over whom the ball passed, presumably on the basis of where it eventually came to rest. An alternative thesis was put forward by a cynical wag, signing himself Q.E.D. in his correspondence with *Golf*. He attributed the drive's phenomenal length to "dogs or crows which have often been known to carry Golf-balls some distance and drop them".

The story of Freddie's refutation of Peter Guthrie's theories is apocryphal rather than anecdotal. His familiarity with his father's researches probably did not extend beyond what he gleaned on those occasions he was called on to help to estimate the initial velocity. J. L. Low, the biographer of both Peter Guthrie and Freddie Tait reviewed the anecdote in these words (Low, 1902):

> "There is a story that Freddie demolished his father's arguments by driving a ball further than the limit that had been set by the Professor. Freddie perhaps half believed that he had created this joke against 'the Governor'', for he never studied his father's articles very closely, as we can judge from

the fact that it is not till the end of 1898 that we find him writing to Jack (Tait's eldest son) to announce that 'the Governor's theory is underspin.' The grain of truth that was in the story was made into a good jest by the facile pen of Mr Andrew Lang".

That is, Freddie's understanding of his father's work may have come from reading the 1896 paper which was delayed until October 1898, and the anecdote was in large measure the product of a journalist's imagination.

Afterword

The subject of this article was also the basis of a paper delivered at the conference, 'Peter Guthrie Tait (1831–1901): Centenary Meeting', held at the Royal Society of Edinburgh (2 July 2001). The authors are pictured either side of June Barrow-Green, holding a golf iron with an adjustable angle of club-face that Tait designed for his experiments (taken from *BSHM Newsletter* 44 (Autumn 2001), p. 15).

References

Hoerner, S. F. 1965 *Fluid Dynamic Drag*, Private publication, Bricktown N. J., second edition, 1965.

Low, J. L. *F. G. Tait, A Record: A moving story of F.G. Tait, Scotland's greatest hero, as gallant on the golf course as on the battlefield*, London: J Nisbet, 1900.

Macfarlane, A. *Lectures on Ten British Physicists of the Nineteenth Century*, New York: Wiley, 1919.

Further reading

To learn more of the life and achievements of Peter Guthrie Tait, including his topology of knots and his promotion of quaternions (a precursor of vectors), see my essay at the James Clerk Maxwell Foundation website:
Prichard, C., 'Aspects of the life and work of Peter Guthrie Tait, FRSE', https://clerkmaxwellfoundation.org/PritchardTaitBooklet.pdf